THE Calvin and HobbES

TENTH ANNIVERSARY BOOK

OTHER BOOKS BY BILL WATTERSON

Calvin and Hobbes
Something Under the Bed Is Drooling
Yukon Ho!
Weirdos From Another Planet!
The Revenge of the Baby-Sat
Scientific Progress Goes "Boink"
Attack of the Deranged Mutant Killer Monster Snow Goons
The Days Are Just *Packed*
Homicidal Psycho Jungle Cat

TREASURY COLLECTIONS

The Essential Calvin and Hobbes
The Calvin and Hobbes Lazy Sunday Book
The Authoritative Calvin and Hobbes
The Indispensable Calvin and Hobbes

THE Calvin aNd HobbES

TENTH ANNIVERSARY BOOK

by Bill Watterson

SCHOLASTIC INC.
New York Toronto London Auckland Sydney

Calvin and Hobbes is distributed internationally by Universal Press Syndicate.

ISBN 0-590-50827-X

12 11 10 9 8 7   7 8 9/9 0/0

Printed in the U.S.A.   14

First Scholastic printing, November 1995

ACKNOWLEDGEMENTS

BLONDIE © 1990 King Features Syndicate. Reprinted with special permission of King Features Syndicate.

FOXTROT © 1990 Bill Amend. Reprinted with permission of Universal Press Syndicate. All rights reserved.

HEATHCLIFF © 1990 Tribune Media Services, Inc. Reprinted with permission of Tribune Media Service, Inc.

THE LOCKHORNS © 1990 King Features Syndicate. Reprinted with special permission of King Features Syndicate.

THE WIZARD OF ID © 1990 Johnny Hart. Reprinted with special permission of Johnny Hart and Creators Syndicate.

The front page of the comics section of the *Chicago Sunday Tribune* of May 31, 1931, is reprinted with the special permission of the *Chicago Tribune.*

The page from the comics section of *The Philadelphia Inquirer* of September 30, 1990, is reprinted with the special permission of *The Philadelphia Inquirer.*

TO MELISSA

THE COMICS IN TRANSITION

Comics are a wonderfully versatile medium. With the potent combination of words and pictures, the comic strip can depict anything a cartoonist has the imagination to envision.

Of course, the newspaper business puts severe constraints on comic strips. Comics are produced on an inflexible daily deadline and are given very little space for writing or drawing. Moreover, because comics are frequently assumed to be children's entertainment, and because comics must attract a huge and diverse readership to be profitable, there are editorial constraints as well: controversial subjects and opinions are rarely tolerated. The commercial, mass-market needs of newspapers are not often sympathetic to the concerns of artistic expression.

It is difficult for a new strip to get into newspapers, and few strips survive long even then. Newspapers already have their comics pages filled with popular strips, and the only way for a paper to bring in a new strip is to dump an old strip. The new strip must quickly establish itself in the hearts of readers, or it's the first one to go when another new strip comes along. The competition far exceeds the available spaces, and the results are Darwinian.

The top strips, however, can go on decade after decade. *Blondie* has been in the papers for sixty-five years, and *Beetle Bailey*, *Dennis the Menace*, and *Peanuts* are all in their forties. Even *Doonesbury* has been around for twenty-five years—that is to say, a quarter of the comics' entire existence. There is very little turnover at the top of this business. The most popular strips become institutions and can hold their spaces in the paper for generations.

I think the permanence of familiar strips and the lack of change *within* the strips account for much of their popularity. In a newspaper full of surprising horrors, it's a comforting little ritual to see our favorite characters each morning for a few seconds over coffee. They become friends of sorts. We care about them when they're in trouble, and we count on them to look at life with a slightly amusing twist that may even help us do the same. They are there for us seven days a week, year after year.

Adding to that consistency, comic characters typically stay the same age and maintain the same appearance (often right down to the same outfit every day), no matter how things change in the real world. In most strips, certain predictable events and situations recur frequently with only minor variations. In most strips, every story can be expected to end with the characters right back where they began. In most strips, the regular cast is unvarying. The world of a comic strip is simple and enduring, a tiny oasis of stability in a mixed-up, ever-changing world.

Or, at least they used to be. Lately, more strips have been addressing controversial subjects, and there have been sabbaticals, early retirements, size and format demands, and fights over issues of creative control. Some commentators (including a few cartoonists) explain these recent events as the self-indulgent tantrums of the profession's nine-hundred-pound gorillas, but I believe these critics are missing the bigger picture. On the hundredth anniversary of the American newspaper comic strip, the comics are in a period of major transition.

The first transition is a simple one: the comics are beginning one of their rare generation shifts. When a popular strip can easily last forty or fifty years, the top cartoonists define the profession that long. Cartoonists who started in the 1950s and 1960s changed the direction of the comic strip and have set the standards ever since. Recently, new talents have worked their ways to the top ranks, bringing along some different ideas about what cartooning should be.

The second transition is one of artistic interpretation. Over the course of the last century, the line between commercial art and fine art has been greatly blurred. Whereas original comic strip drawings were once given away to fans or were destroyed to save storage space, today original cartoons are sold in galleries for hundreds or thousands of dollars. Whereas cartoonists were once considered replaceable workers, now—in certain cases—syndicates are recognizing that only the original creator is capable of producing the strip's unique vision. Academics now write about the comics as social history and commentary. There are several cartoon collections and museums. Comics have been awarded Pulitzer prizes. Whether or not most comics are Great Art can be debated, but there is no denying that cartoonists and the public take the comics more seriously than they used to. Increasingly, cartoonists are regarding their creations as a form of personal expression. Issues of creative control are becoming relevant to cartoonists, and old assumptions about the way business is conducted are being questioned.

Third, the newspaper business itself is changing. The comics were invented in the late 1800s, when large cities had as many as a half-dozen newspapers, each trying to outdo the other to attract the readership of huge new immigrant populations. The comics were visual, easy to understand, funny, boisterous, and lowbrow by design and hence immediately popular. Cartoonists had few pretensions about the artistic or cultural significance of their work. From the beginning, the comics were regarded as a commercial product that existed for the purpose of increasing newspaper readership. Cartoonists considered themselves newspapermen, not artists. Their job, pure and simple, was to help sell newspapers.

Since that time:

• *Syndicates have turned the comics into big business.* At first, cartoonists were hired by individual newspapers to produce comics exclusively for that paper. Today, cartoonists work for syndicates that sell their strips to newspapers worldwide. That means a strip today needs very broad appeal. Whereas the early cartoonists experimented, starting and stopping strips as their interests changed and discovering what appealed to the local audience along the way, syndication has encouraged the calculated production of strips to mirror trends and capitalize on the specific interests of desirable demographic groups. Marketing strips on a large scale encourages comics to be conservative, easily categorized, and imitative of previous successes. The comics have gained immense readerships and have become very profitable this way, but at some cost to the comics' early exuberance.

• *There is now much less newspaper competition.* Each big city used to have several papers battling each other for readers, and a well-liked comic strip could dramatically help a paper's circulation. Popular strips would go to the highest bidding newspaper, and the other papers would scramble to buy other strips that might help them compete. Today, most cities have just one newspaper, and the surviving paper can have any strip it wants. It will obviously buy the most popular strips, and without other papers to grab other strips, the big strips get huge, and the small strips play musical chairs and vanish. There is little room any more for a peculiar "cult" strip with a small but devoted following. There are fewer openings for new strips, fewer opportunities for marginal strips to survive, and there is less time for a strip to find its audience.

• *Television has replaced newspapers as the source of most people's information.* Newspaper production costs have gone up, circulations have not, and some of the big advertising accounts have abandoned newspapers. A comic strip might once have lured readers from one newspaper to another, but comics don't lure people away from televisions. The comics are less helpful to newspapers than they used to be, so papers look at the comics page as one more place to cut costs. They cram more strips into less space, forcing cartoonists to write and draw more simply to stay legible. With fewer words and cruder drawings, the comics become less imaginative and less entertaining. The irony of this is that newspapers are desperate to attract readers reared on the visual impact of television. Papers have spent a lot of money to improve layouts and add colorful maps, charts, and photographs, while the comics—the one graphic feature unique to newspapers—typically languish on a single page of tiny black-and-white boxes arranged in a boring grid. By unimaginatively imposing standardized, reduced formats on all comics, papers give the comics cost-efficient space, not graphically effective space.

Because of all these developments, the traditional relationship between cartoonist, syndicate, and newspaper has been strained. As circumstances change, each party tries to protect its own interests. Newspapers are trimming costs by cutting space and features. Syndicates respond by diversifying into licensing and publishing. The top cartoonists are demanding greater control over their work, and some are leaving the business altogether. With fewer common goals and needs, there is less trust and cooperation.

As a cartoonist who's done his share of aggravating the situation, it seems to me that good comics are in the interest of readers, newspapers, syndicates, and cartoonists. Yet the best strips of the past would have a tough time in newspapers today. The esoteric but brilliant *Krazy Kat,* barely marketable in its own day, would be hard pressed to find a publisher willing to champion its unique vision today. Adventure strips like *Terry and the Pirates* would be unlikely to sweep readers into their exotic stories now that beautiful illustration is stifled by the little boxes available to strips. *Popeye* relied on up to twenty panels on Sunday to create its raucous energy, a sheer impossibility in today's quarter-page Sunday slots. Continuous "soap opera" strips are all but gone now, unable to keep their plots gripping with the reduction of dialogue necessary in small panels. The comics are losing their variety.

Sixty years ago, the best strips weren't just amusingly drawn, they were beautiful to look at. I can't think of a single strip today that comes close to that standard of craftsmanship. Now we have plenty of simply drawn gag strips, but not much else. We've lost an essential part of what makes comics fun to read. As animated cartoons and comic books are becoming more sophisticated, more lavishly produced, and more popular than ever, newspaper comic strips are enervated.

I've heard it argued that today's readers do not have the patience for involved storylines and rich artwork in comics anymore. Popularity polls are cited to show that comics are doing just fine the way they are. I disagree and I think it's a mistake to underestimate readers' appetite for quality. The comics can be much more than they presently are. Better strips could attract larger audiences, and this would help newspapers. The comics' potential—as a seller of newspapers, and as an art form—is great if cartoonists will challenge themselves to create extraordinary work and if the business will work to create a sustaining environment for it.

LICENSING

Comic strips have been licensed from the beginning, but today the merchandising of popular cartoon characters is more profitable than ever. Derivative products—dolls, T-shirts, TV specials, and so on—can turn the right strip into a gold mine. Everyone is looking for the next Snoopy or Garfield, and Calvin and Hobbes were imagined to be the perfect candidates. The more I thought about licensing, however, the less I liked it. I spent nearly five years fighting my syndicate's pressure to merchandise my creation.

In an age of shameless commercialism, my objections to licensing are not widely shared. Many cartoonists view the comic strip as a commercial product itself, so they regard licensing as a natural extension of their work. As most people

ask, what's wrong with comic strip characters appearing on calendars and coffee mugs? If people want to buy the stuff, why not give it to them?

I have several problems with licensing. First of all, I believe licensing usually cheapens the original creation. When cartoon characters appear on countless products, the public inevitably grows bored and irritated with them, and the appeal and value of the original work are diminished. Nothing dulls the edge of a new and clever cartoon like saturating the market with it.

Second, commercial products rarely respect how a comic strip works. A wordy, multiple-panel strip with extended conversation and developed personalities does not condense to a coffee mug illustration without great violation to the strip's spirit. The subtleties of a multi-dimensional strip are sacrificed for the one-dimensional needs of the product. The world of a comic strip ought to be a special place with its own logic and life. I don't want some animation studio giving Hobbes an actor's voice, and I don't want some greeting card company using Calvin to wish people a happy anniversary, and I don't want the issue of Hobbes's reality settled by a doll manufacturer. When everything fun and magical is turned into something for sale, the strip's world is diminished. *Calvin and Hobbes* was designed to be a comic strip and that's all I want it to be. It's the one place where everything works the way I intend it to.

Third, as a practical matter, licensing requires a staff of assistants to do the work. The cartoonist must become a factory foreman, delegating responsibilities and overseeing the production of things he does not create. Some cartoonists don't mind this, but I went into cartooning to draw cartoons, not to run a corporate empire. I take great pride in the fact that I write every word, draw every line, color every Sunday strip, and paint every book illustration myself. My strip is a low-tech, one-man operation, and I like it that way. I believe it's the only way to preserve the craft and to keep the strip personal. Despite what some cartoonists say, approving someone else's work is not the same as doing it yourself.

Beyond all this, however, lies a deeper issue: the corruption of a strip's integrity. All strips are supposed to be entertaining, but some strips have a point of view and a serious purpose behind the jokes. When the cartoonist is trying to talk honestly and seriously about life, then I believe he has a responsibility to think beyond satisfying the market's every whim and desire. Cartoonists who think they can be taken seriously as artists while using the strip's protagonists to sell boxer shorts are deluding themselves.

The world of a comic strip is much more fragile than most people realize or will admit. Believable characters are hard to develop and easy to destroy. When a cartoonist licenses his characters, his voice is co-opted by the business concerns of toy makers, television producers, and advertisers. The cartoonist's job is no longer to be an original thinker; his job is to keep his characters profitable. The characters become "celebrities," endorsing companies and products, avoiding controversy, and saying whatever someone will pay them to say. At that point, the strip has no soul. With its integrity gone, a strip loses its deeper significance.

My strip is about private realities, the magic of imagination, and the specialness of certain friendships. Who would believe in the innocence of a little kid and his tiger if they cashed in on their popularity to sell overpriced knickknacks that nobody needs? Who would trust the honesty of the strip's observations when the characters are hired out as advertising hucksters? If I were to undermine my own characters like this, I would have taken the rare privilege of being paid to express my own ideas and given it up to be an ordinary salesman and a hired illustrator. I would have sold out my own creation. I have no use for that kind of cartooning.

Unfortunately, the more popular *Calvin and Hobbes* became, the less control I had over its fate. I was presented with licensing possibilities before the strip was even a year old, and the pressure to capitalize on its success mounted from then on. Succeeding beyond anyone's wildest expectations had only inspired wilder expectations.

To put the problem simply, trainloads of money were at stake—millions and millions of dollars could be made with a few signatures. Syndicates are businesses, and no business passes up that kind of opportunity without an argument.

Undermining my position, I had signed a contract giving my syndicate all exploitation rights to *Calvin and Hobbes* into the next century. Because it is virtually impossible to get into daily newspapers without a syndicate, it is standard practice for syndicates to use their superior bargaining position to demand rights they neither need nor deserve when contracting with unknown cartoonists. The cartoonist has few alternatives to the syndicate's terms: he can take his work elsewhere on the unlikely chance that a different syndicate would be more inclined to offer concessions, he can self-syndicate and attempt to attract the interest of newspapers without the benefit of reputation or contacts, or he can go back home and find some other job. Universal would not sell my strip to newspapers unless I gave the syndicate the right to merchandise the strip in other media. At the time, I had not thought much about licensing and the issue was not among my top concerns. Two syndicates had already rejected *Calvin and Hobbes*, and I worried more about the contractual consequences if the strip failed than the contractual consequences if the strip succeeded. Eager for the opportunity to publish my work, I signed the contract, and it was not until later, when the pressure to commercialize focused my opinions on the matter, that I understood the trouble I'd gotten myself into.

I had no legal recourse to stop the syndicate from licensing. The syndicate preferred to have my cooperation, but my approval was by no means necessary. Our arguments with each other grew more bitter as the stakes got higher, and we had an ugly relationship for several years.

The debate had its ridiculous aspects. I am probably the only cartoonist who resented the popularity of his own strip. Most cartoonists are more than eager for the exposure, wealth, and prestige that licensing offers. When cartoonists fight their syndicates, it's usually to make more money, not

less. And making the whole issue even more absurd, when I didn't license, bootleg *Calvin and Hobbes* merchandise sprung up to feed the demand. Mall stores openly sold T-shirts with drawings illegally lifted from my books, and obscene or drug-related shirts were rife on college campuses. Only thieves and vandals have made money on *Calvin and Hobbes* merchandise.

For years, Universal pressured me to compromise on a "limited" licensing program. The syndicate would agree to rule out the most offensive products if I would agree to go along with the rest. This would be, in essence, my only shot at controlling what happened to my work. The idea of bartering principles was offensive to me and I refused to compromise. For that matter, the syndicate and I had nothing to trade anyway: I didn't care if we made more money, and the syndicate didn't care about my notions of artistic integrity. With neither of us valuing what the other had to offer, compromise was impossible. One of us was going to trample the interests of the other.

By the strip's fifth year, the debate had gone as far as it could possibly go, and I prepared to quit. If I could not control what *Calvin and Hobbes* stood for, the strip was worthless to me. My contract was so one-sided that quitting would have allowed Universal to replace me with hired writers and artists and license my creation anyway, but at this point, the syndicate agreed to renegotiate my contract. The exploitation rights to the strip were returned to me, and I will not license *Calvin and Hobbes*.

SABBATICALS

I never expected, much less demanded, time off from the strip, but exhausted and disgusted after the licensing fight, I readily accepted the syndicate's offer of two nine-month sabbaticals. By taking them within three years of each other, I became the Lazy Cartoonist poster boy, but in fact, I am not a big advocate of long breaks, or for that matter, of reruns.

Garry Trudeau and Gary Larson had previously taken sabbaticals, so I became the third cartoonist to announce a long break from his strip. Some other cartoonists have publicly denounced these vacations as unnecessary and self-indulgent. I find these criticisms incredibly presumptuous. Some cartoonists can meet their own standards of quality and be on the golf course by noon, but that's not the case for everyone. In my opinion, any creative person can be forgiven some occasional time off to recharge the batteries and pursue other interests.

That said, sabbaticals definitely strain the cartoonist's relationship with newspaper editors and readers. Reruns are tedious, and after several months of them, there is always the risk that readers will break their habit of reading the strip and discover that they don't miss it. Editors, of course, don't like paying for the same material twice, and with such limited space for comics and great competition among new strips, an editor can hardly be blamed for dropping the reruns and substituting a fresher strip. To justify their place in the newspaper, the reruns have to be more popular than the other strips available as a replacement. This is one reason why there will never be many sabbaticals.

A better solution, obviously, is periodic short vacations. To its credit, this last year Universal Press Syndicate offered *all* its cartoonists four weeks off each year. Each cartoonist can decide for himself the need for time off and the risk of stopping the strip. With more frequent breaks, cartoonists may be able to preserve their sanity without long sabbaticals, and readers and editors will undoubtedly find shorter periods of reruns less irritating. I think this is more reasonable all around.

THE SUNDAY STRIP

The format for Sunday strips is a rigid one, and as *Calvin and Hobbes* became more visually complex, I found that I could not design the strip to the story's best advantage. I would often need to eliminate dialogue or simplify the drawings so they'd fit in the arbitrary space the format allotted. At times, this threatened to ruin the idea, and it frequently made for an ugly, graceless strip. It aggravated me to think that I could draw a better strip than my readers were seeing, so I took advantage of my first sabbatical to propose a newly designed Sunday strip.

The prevailing Sunday format was invented to standardize comic strip layouts so as to give newspapers the utmost flexibility in printing them. The strip is drawn in three rows. Printed full size, this will fill half a newspaper page. Most papers are reluctant to run a strip that big, so they remove the top row of panels, which makes the strip take up only a third of a page. Because the cartoonist cannot count on readers seeing the top panels, he must waste them on "throw-away" gags that have little to do with the rest of the strip. To make the strip smaller still, editors can reduce the panels and line them up in two rows, so the strip takes only a quarter of a page. Some papers cut and reduce even more, at which point the strip is virtually illegible. To neatly accommodate all these variations, the panel divisions are specific and unyielding. The strip will fit the different space needs of different newspapers this way, but the cartoonist loses the ability to design his strip effectively.

Before all this, up until the 1940s, a Sunday strip often filled an *entire* newspaper page. I don't think it's coincidental that this was the "golden age" of comics. With all that space to fill, cartoonists produced works of extraordinary beauty and power. There has been nothing remotely like them since. It seemed to me that if readers in the 1990s were given a glimpse

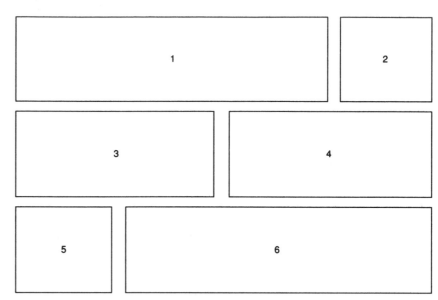

Sunday format as 1/2 page.

of what they'd been missing, they might read the comics with more interest, and this would benefit newspapers. I believed I could offer newspapers a better cartoon for their money.

Universal agreed to sell my strip exclusively as a half-page feature with no panel restrictions. I was thrilled, but the syndicate warned me that many newspapers would balk at being told they couldn't reduce and rearrange my work anymore. We talked in terms of losing half my Sunday client list, but I figured it would be worth the loss in income if I could work at the limits of my abilities for a change.

The syndicate was right: a number of editors were enraged. They threw syndicate sales people out of their offices and inundated Universal with cancellation threats.

Editors informed me that cartoonists had no business making space decisions on their behalf. They reminded me that newspaper space was expensive and the industry was

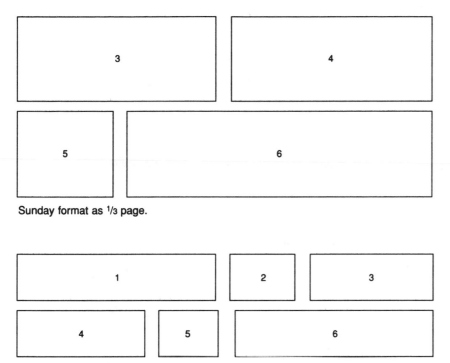

Sunday format as 1/3 page.

Sunday format as 1/4 page.

struggling already. They worried what ridiculous demands would come next if this became a precedent. They pointed out that they had just paid for nine months of reruns. They argued that, so long as they paid for the strip, it should serve their needs, not mine. They questioned my familiarity with the real world and wondered if my ego had any boundaries at all. They threatened to cancel other Universal features in wholesale retaliation. They insisted that other popular strips would have to be canceled to make room for mine and that this was an unconscionable grab for more of the newspaper. On this last point, several cartoonists joined in.

I was sorry to see that none of these objections addressed the issue of the graphic needs of comic strips. I also thought it

was a curious oversight that no one bothered to ask what newspaper readers thought of a larger Sunday *Calvin and Hobbes*.

I still believe that the editors' response was poorly reasoned and absurdly hot-tempered. I was in no way telling editors what to do. I was simply establishing the conditions upon which I would sell my work, just as one sets a price. If an editor found my conditions unacceptable, he was perfectly free to cancel my strip and run something else. Any pressure he felt to take my strip came from his paper's readers, not from me, and I do not apologize for offering papers a popular strip.

I also believe that with a little imagination, most Sunday comic sections could be redesigned to run one half-page strip without dumping others. Moreover, I expected my strip would be canceled in many papers, and that would have opened those spaces to other cartoonists.

And as for my sinister motives and my insensitivity to the newspaper industry's struggles, I can only argue that I was willing to do more work for less income, and I could easily have gotten more freedom *and* more money by abandoning newspapers altogether and publishing elsewhere.

With a firestorm of ill will directed at the syndicate, Universal compromised on the size issue and offered the strip two ways: as the half-page and as a much reduced version of the same thing. I was disappointed, but this still freed me from the panel constraints of the old format. I do not have to waste any panels on throw-away gags and I can design the space more effectively, even if the whole strip is ultimately reduced. Very few papers canceled, but many took the smaller strip. In some cases, this means *Calvin and Hobbes* actually lost space.

Despite that setback, with this new format I've drawn many strips I never could have drawn before. In some of my new Sunday strips, I've been able to draw large panels or as many as twenty small panels, and that has opened up new ways of storytelling. I do many wordless Sunday strips now,

Sample Sunday Page, *Chicago Tribune*, May 31, 1931.

Sample Sunday Page, *The Philadelphia Inquirer*,
September 30, 1990.

because the drawings can finally hold their own. I think I've been able to make Calvin's world more vivid, and I think I've made the space more exciting to look at. These are not esoteric concerns; these are what make a comic strip fun to read.

Over the last several decades, comic strips have been reduced and reduced and reduced. Cartoonists have acquiesced, believing that cutting everyone's size is better than cutting the number of strips a paper will print. Up to a point, that's true, but I think the reductions have now gone so far as to take a serious toll on the art. The possibilities for expression are diminishing, and as a consequence, we don't have well-drawn comics any more. It's hard for me to argue that maintaining the quantity of comics is a reasonable substitute for maintaining their quality.

INFLUENCES

Three comic strips have been tremendously inspirational to me: *Peanuts* by Charles Schulz, *Pogo* by Walt Kelly, and *Krazy Kat* by George Herriman. These strips have very different sensibilities, but they've helped me discover what a comic strip can do.

Peanuts books were among the first things I ever read, and once I saw them, I knew I wanted to be a cartoonist. I instantly related to the flat, spare drawings, the honesty of the children's insecurities, and to Snoopy's bizarre and separate world. At the time, I didn't appreciate how innovative all that was—I just knew it had a kind of humor and truth that other strips lacked. Now when I reread the old books, I'm amazed at what a melancholy comic strip it was in the '60s. Surely no

other strip has presented a world so relentlessly cruel and heartless. Charlie Brown's self-torture in the face of constant failure is funny in a bitter, hopelessly sad way. I think the most important thing I learned from *Peanuts* is that a comic strip can have an emotional edge to it and that it can talk about the big issues of life in a sensitive and perceptive way.

Pogo, in some ways, is the opposite of *Peanuts*. Whereas *Peanuts* is a visually spare strip about private insecurities, *Pogo* was a lushly drawn strip, full of bombast and physical commotion. The strip's dialogue was a stew of dialect, pun, and nonsense, and word balloons were often filled with gothic type or circus poster letters to suggest the character's personality and voice. With the possible exception of Porkypine, there was not a soul-searching character in a cast of dozens. The drawings were beautifully animated and the stories wandered down back roads, got lost, and forgot their destinations. Kelly's animals satirized the day's politics, back when comics were expected to avoid controversy altogether. Beneath the chaos and bluster though, the strip had a basic faith in human decency and an optimism for bumbling through. *Pogo* had a pace and an atmosphere that will probably never be seen again. The strip is a wonderful lesson in what a lively, rich world the comics can present.

It is *Krazy Kat*, however, that fills me with the most awe today. *Krazy Kat* is more poetic than funny, with a charm that's impossible to describe. Everything about the strip is idiosyncratic and peculiar—the wonderful, scratchy drawings, the bold design and color of the Sunday strips, the kooky, austere Arizona landscapes, and the bizarre conglomeration of Spanish, slang, literary allusion, dialect, and mispronunciation that makes up the dialogue. The circular plot, such as it is, can be interpreted (and over-interpreted) as an allegory about good and evil, love and hate, society and individual . . . or it can simply be enjoyed for its lunatic machinery. For me, the magic of the strip is not so much in what it says, but how it says it. In its singular, uncompromised vision, its subtle whimsy and its odd beauty, *Krazy Kat* stands alone.

Other cartoonists and artists have inspired me as well, but these three strips shaped my idea of what a comic strip could be. All the strips work on several levels, entertaining while they deal with bigger issues of life. Most important, these strips reflect uniquely personal views of the world. They argue that comics can be vehicles for beautiful artwork and serious, intelligent expression. They set the example I wanted to follow.

The challenge of any cartoonist is not just to duplicate the achievements of the past, but to build on them as well. Comic strips have a short history, but their traditions are important. Cartoonists learn about cartooning by reading cartoons. Unfortunately, the history of comics is not very accessible. Popular strips were not regularly collected in books until very recently. *Peanuts* and *Pogo* collections are often difficult to find and are increasingly expensive. *Krazy Kat* still has not been adequately published in book form. It has only been in the last few years that I've seen any extended runs of the true classics of the medium. Early strips are amazing—some are far more inventive than today's—but they can't educate future cartoonists if they're not collected and republished. Sometimes I wonder what strips would be like if every generation didn't have to reinvent the wheel.

THE PROCESS

I think I learned to be a writer so I could draw for a living. Actually, I enjoy writing as much as drawing, but working on a deadline, the drawing is easier and faster.

People always ask how cartoonists come up with ideas, and the answer is so boring that we're usually tempted to make up something sarcastic. The truth is, we hold a blank sheet of paper, stare into space, and let our minds wander. (To the layman, this looks remarkably like goofing off.) When something interests us, we play around with it. Sometimes this yields a funny observation; sometimes it doesn't, but that's about all there is to it. Once in a while the cartoonist will find himself in a beam of light and angels will appear with a great idea, but not often.

Occasionally I'll have a subject or issue in mind that I want to talk about, but if I don't have a ready topic, I try to think of what I'd like to draw. My goal is to feel enthusiastic about some aspect of the work. I think one can always tell when an artist is engaged and having a good time: the energy and life comes through in the work. I like to sit outside when I write, partly because it seems less like a job that way, and partly because there are bugs and birds and rocks around that may suggest an idea. I never know what will trigger a workable idea, so my writing schedule varies a great deal. Sometimes I can write several strips in an afternoon; sometimes I can't write anything at all. I never know if another hour sitting there will be wasted time or the most productive hour of the day.

When I come up with a topic, I look at it through Calvin's

eyes. Calvin's personality dictates a range of possible reactions to any subject, so I just tag along and see what he does. The truth of the matter is that my characters write their own material. I put them in situations and listen to them. A line for Hobbes never works for Calvin or Susie, because Hobbes reacts differently and he expresses himself in a different voice. Virtually all the strip's humor comes from the characters' personalities: I would never think of Calvin's retort if Calvin weren't the one saying it.

I write my ideas in an ordinary school notebook. I spend a lot of time fussing with the wording, juggling the various concerns of timing, clarity, brevity, and so on. I write in pencil, and go through erasers at an alarming rate. Once I bang an idea into form, I make a small doodle of the characters to give the strip a rough outline. My purpose at this point is mostly to show who's speaking each line, but I try to suggest gestures and rough compositions, so I will think about the idea in visual terms when it comes time to ink it up. I reevaluate the roughs over several days, when I'm fresher and more objective. Often the writing needs more work, and sometimes I just cross the whole thing out. On occasion, I've ripped up entire stories—weeks of material—that I didn't think were good. Obviously, if I'm right on deadline, that kind of editing becomes a luxury, so I try to write well ahead of due dates. It's very embarrassing to send out a strip I think is bad, so I like a long lead time and, given the need to fill newspaper space every day, I weed out as much mediocre work as possible.

After I have about thirty daily strips, I show them to my wife. She can usually intuit what I'm trying to say, even when I don't get it right, so she's a good editor, and a pretty accurate Laugh-o-meter. After reworking or scrapping weak strips, I ink up the ones I like.

I typically ink six daily strips, or one Sunday strip, in a long day. I'd enjoy the inking more if I could take more time,

but I need to draw efficiently in order to gain back the time lost writing bad ideas. I lightly pencil in the dialogue first, as that determines the space left for drawing. Next, I sketch in the characters very loosely, establishing the composition of each panel. I frequently make revisions, so I use a light pencil and I erase as needed. If the picture is unusually complex, I'll render the difficult parts completely, but generally, I try to do as little pencil work as possible. That way, the inking stays spontaneous and fun, because I'm not simply tracing pencil lines. Inking mistakes and accidents are whited out.

I draw the strip with a small sable brush and waterproof India ink on Strathmore bristol board. I letter the dialogue with a Rapidograph fountain pen, and I use a crowquill pen for odds and ends. It's about as low-tech as you can get.

The Sunday strips also need to be colored. This is a time-consuming and rather tedious task, but the color is an integral part of my Sunday strips, so I think it's important to choose all the colors myself. (Foreign collections of my work are sometimes recolored, and the results rarely please me.) When I first started *Calvin and Hobbes*, there were 64 colors available for Sunday strips; now we have 125 colors, as well as the ability to fade colors into each other. The colors are incremental percentage combinations of red, yellow, and blue, and we have a pretty good range, although I wish there were more pale colors. Each color has a number, so I color my strip on an overlay, and mark the corresponding numbers. The syndicate sends this to American Color, a company that processes all the Sunday comics into color negatives for newspaper printing.

After a batch of strips is inked and colored, I send them to the syndicate, where my editor corrects my spelling and grammar, and looks for anything offensive. A copyright sticker is affixed and the strip is printed up and sent to subscribing newspapers. Then I start writing again.

THE CAST

Calvin: Calvin is named for a sixteenth-century theologian who believed in predestination. Most people assume that Calvin is based on a son of mine, or based on detailed memories of my own childhood. In fact, I don't have children, and I was a fairly quiet, obedient kid—almost Calvin's opposite. One of the reasons that Calvin's character is fun to write is that I often don't agree with him.

Calvin is autobiographical in the sense that he thinks about the same issues that I do, but in this, Calvin reflects my adulthood more than my childhood. Many of Calvin's struggles are metaphors for my own. I suspect that most of us get old without growing up, and that inside every adult (sometimes not very far inside) is a bratty kid who wants everything his own way. I use Calvin as an outlet for my immaturity, as a way to keep myself curious about the natural world, as a way to ridicule my own obsessions, and as a way to comment on human nature. I wouldn't want Calvin in my house, but on paper, he helps me sort through my life and understand it.

Hobbes: Named after a seventeenth-century philosopher with a dim view of human nature, Hobbes has the patient dignity and common sense of most animals I've met. Hobbes was very much inspired by one of our cats, a gray tabby named Sprite. Sprite not only provided the long body and facial characteristics for Hobbes, she also was the model for his personality. She was good-natured, intelligent, friendly, and enthusiastic in a sneaking-up-and-pouncing sort of way. Sprite suggested the idea of Hobbes greeting Calvin at the door in midair at high velocity.

With most cartoon animals, the humor comes from their humanlike behavior. Hobbes stands upright and talks of course, but I try to preserve his feline side, both in his physical demeanor and his attitude. His reserve and tact seem very catlike to me, along with his barely contained pride in not being human. Like Calvin, I often prefer the company of animals to people, and Hobbes is my idea of an ideal friend.

The so-called "gimmick" of my strip—the two versions of Hobbes—is sometimes misunderstood. I don't think of Hobbes as a doll that miraculously comes to life when Calvin's around. Neither do I think of Hobbes as the product of Calvin's imagination. The nature of Hobbes's reality doesn't interest me, and each story goes out of its way to avoid resolving the issue. Calvin sees Hobbes one way, and everyone else sees Hobbes another way. I show two versions of reality, and each makes complete sense to the participant who sees it. I think that's how life works. None of us sees the world in exactly the same way, and I just draw that literally in the strip. Hobbes is more about the subjective nature of reality than about dolls coming to life.

Calvin's parents: I've never given Calvin's parents names, because as far as the strip is concerned, they are important only as Calvin's mom and dad. Calvin's dad has been rumored to be a self-portrait. All my characters are half me, so it's true in some ways, but Calvin's dad is also partly a satire of my own father. Any strip about how suffering "builds character" is usually a verbatim transcript of my dad's explanations for why we were all freezing, exhausted, hungry, and lost on camping trips. These things are a lot funnier after twenty-five years have passed.

Calvin's mom is the daily disciplinarian, a job that taxes her sanity, so I don't think we get to see her at her best. I regret that the strip mostly shows her impatient side, but I try to hint at other aspects of her personality and her interests by what she's doing when Calvin barges in.

Early on, Calvin's parents were criticized by readers for being unloving and needlessly sarcastic. (Calvin's dad has remarked that what he really wanted was a dog.) At the time, I think it was unusual for a comic strip to concentrate on the exasperating aspects of kids without a lot of hugs and sentimentality to leaven it. We usually only see Calvin's parents when they're reacting to Calvin, so as secondary characters, I've tried to keep them realistic, with a reasonable sense of humor about having a kid like Calvin. I think they do a better job than I would.

Susie Derkins: Susie is earnest, serious, and smart—the kind of girl I was attracted to in school and eventually married. "Derkins" was the nickname of my wife's family's beagle. The early strips with Susie were heavy-handed with the love-hate conflict, and it's taken me a while to get a bead on Susie's relationship with Calvin. I suspect Calvin has a mild crush on her that he expresses by trying to annoy her, but Susie is a bit unnerved and put off by Calvin's weirdness. This encourages Calvin to be even weirder, so it's a good dynamic. Neither of them quite understands what's going on, which is probably true of most relationships. I sometimes imagine a strip from Susie's point of view would be interesting, and after so many strips about boys, I think a strip about a little girl, drawn by a woman, could be great.

Miss Wormwood: As a few readers guessed, Miss Wormwood is named after the apprentice devil in C. S. Lewis's *The Screwtape Letters*. I have a lot of sympathy for Miss Wormwood. We see hints that she's waiting to retire, that she smokes too much, and that she takes a lot of medication. I think she seriously believes in the value of education, so needless to say, she's an unhappy person.

Moe: Moe is every jerk I've ever known. He's big, dumb, ugly, and cruel. I remember school being full of idiots like Moe. I think they spawn on damp locker room floors.

Rosalyn: Probably the only person Calvin fears is his baby-sitter. I put her in a Sunday strip early on, never thinking of her as a regular character, but her intimidation of Calvin surprised me, so she's made a few appearances since. Rosalyn even seems to daunt Calvin's parents, using their desperation to get out of the house to demand advances and raises. Rosalyn's relationship with Calvin is pretty one-dimensional, so baby-sitter stories get harder and harder to write, but for a later addition to the strip, she's worked pretty well.

This was the first *Calvin and Hobbes* strip, published November 18, 1985. At the time, I thought it was important to establish how Calvin and Hobbes got together, but now I think this was unnecessary. Of course, when *Calvin and Hobbes* started, it appeared in about thirty-five newspapers, so not many people saw the first strip anyway. My hometown paper didn't pick up the strip for several months, so I didn't see this strip in the newspaper either. This is one reason I've been grateful for the book collections.

THE GIANT SLIMY OCTOPUS OOZES ACROSS THE BEACH.

HIS HIDEOUS PRESENCE TERRORIZES THE SLEEPY WATERFRONT COMMUNITY.

WITH A SUCKER-COVERED TENTACLE, HE GRABS AN UNSUSPECTING TOURIST.

A MUFFLED SCREAM LINGERS IN THE SALTY AIR!

DID YOU WANT SOMETHING, CALVIN?

ACK
ICK
IG

The look of the strip has changed over the years as the drawings evolved to meet the changing needs of the strip. At the very beginning, the strip had a more cartoony, flat look. The fantasies were originally drawn that way too. At some point, I realized that the fantasies could be drawn in other styles, and, in fact, it added a funny layer to the strip when the fantasies looked more "realistic" than "reality." As the fantasies became more visually complex, I needed the characters to be more three-dimensional, so I could draw them from different perspectives. This gradually changed their appearance.

FISHING IS THE MOST BORING SPORT IN THE WORLD.

WE'VE BEEN SITTING HERE FOR TWENTY MINUTES AND NOT ONE THING HAS HAPPENED!

WAAUGHH

Over the years, Hobbes got sleeker and more catlike, so he could function either horizontally (sneaking up and pouncing) or vertically (walking). In a few early strips, Hobbes had pads on his hands, similar to the pads on his feet. I liked the pads because they made Hobbes's hands look more like paws, but they were visually distracting. Hobbes's hands read better when they were simple and plain white. The strip adapted to its needs by trial and error, and now, the early strips look very strange to me.

In the beginning of a comic strip, the characters are vaguely defined, and they can develop in almost any direction. That's kind of exciting, but the cartoonist can write himself into corners if he's not careful. The characters are established by their actions, so it's important to make choices that won't limit the strip later on. I made a mistake in the early strips by putting Calvin in the Cub Scouts. I originally thought that hiking and camping trips might offer some humorous stories, but the situation was always awkward. Calvin and Hobbes need to be in their own world, so putting a troop of kids around them didn't provide much material. Eventually, I realized that Calvin is not the kind of kid who would join a group anyway. The strips worked against Calvin's personality, so I abandoned them. Later I sent Calvin camping with his family, and that fits the strip's world much better.

The best comics have funny writing and funny drawings, but sometimes the strength of one can make up for the weakness of the other. Great writing will save boring artwork better than great drawings will save boring ideas, but comics are a visual medium, and a funny picture can pull more weight than most people think. Whenever deadlines force me to go with a mediocre idea, I go for broke on the illustration.

This early story lasted only a week, but people wrote worried letters about Hobbes before the story was resolved. It was a good sign that readers were connecting with the characters.

LOST: MY TIGER, "HObbES"

MAYBE YOU SHOULD DESCRIBE HIM.

ON THE QUIET SIDE. SOMEWHAT PECULIAR. A GOOD COMPANION, IN A WEIRD SORT OF WAY.

I MEAN, WHAT DOES HE LOOK LIKE?

OH.

WELL LOOK, SOMEBODY LEFT A STUFFED TIGER OUT IN THE FIELD. HOW STRANGE.

LOOKS LIKE A DOG'S BEEN CHEWING ON YOU, FELLA.

WELL, NOTHING A LITTLE TEA PARTY WITH SOME OTHER STUFFED ANIMALS WOULDN'T HELP. C'MON.

Even at this early date, I was trying to escape the tyranny of panels. Illustrations from this strip were popular for copyright violations.

My wife found a dead kitten outside one morning and this story almost wrote itself. Most of my earlier strips had simple gags, so this was a big departure in tone. Death, of course, is not a common subject for a "kid" strip. This story not only revealed new facets of Calvin's personality but it also suggested to me that the strip was broad enough to handle a wide range of subjects, ideas, and emotions. The strip's world suddenly opened up.

I always enjoy it when Calvin and Hobbes argue. Few strips play with real back-and-forth dialogue. A funny conversation is more interesting to me than a one-liner

Boy, did I get letters about this one. Some readers felt I was maligning adoption by placing it in the same context as child labor and cannibalism. I thought the juxtaposition was ludicrous enough that no one would take it seriously, but as I've learned, some people take *everything* seriously.

Calvin's proportions make for a bizarre skeleton.

Calvin and Hobbes
by WATTERSON

I like the timing on this strip.

...ge from "A Nauseous Nocturne," a poem I did as a special feature ...treasury collection. The treasuries reprinted all the cartoons that the ...ks had already reprinted from the newspaper, so I named the trea- *Essential*, *The Authoritative*, and *The Indispensable Calvin and* ...cause the books were obviously none of these things. In an effort ...treasuries more reason for their existence, I took it upon myself to ...stories and poems for them. Books offer considerably more design ...n newspapers, and I took advantage of the opportunity to paint all ...ions in watercolor, which permitted various subtleties and effects ...dn't get in the Sunday strips. Unfortunately, this was an insane ...extra work on top of the newspaper strip and the other books. ...I do, that I write and draw everything myself, this extra work kept ...petual deadline panic and it wore me into the ground. This exhaust- ...e contributed to the need for a sabbatical several years later.

I rarely laugh when I'm drawing, but I did when I drew the results of Calvin's haircut. I like the contrast of Calvin's and Hobbes's reactions, and as a bonus, this story introduced Tracer Bullet. Would that I could write like this more often.

I CAN'T GET THIS STUPID HAIR TO COMB RIGHT.

SEE HOW IT STICKS OUT IN BACK?

MAYBE YOU NEED A HAIRCUT.

YEAH, BUT BARBERS NEVER CUT IT THE WAY I WANT.

BOY, WHAT A GREAT IDEA! THANKS!

THIS IS EASY! YOU REALLY THINK YOUR MOM WILL PAY ME EIGHT BUCKS?

SO EXACTLY HOW WOULD YOU LIKE THE BACK CUT?

JUST TRIM THE PART THAT STICKS OUT AND TAPER IT A LITTLE.

WOULDN'T YOU RATHER HAVE IT REAL SHORT?

NO, JUST CUT A LITTLE BIT.

ARE YOU SURE? DON'T YOU THINK IT SHOULD BE REAL SHORT? IT LOOKS LIKE IT SHOULD BE REAL SHORT.

ARE YOU TRYING TO TELL ME SOMETHING?

NO, I JUST THINK IT SHOULD BE REAL SHORT. ESPECIALLY, OH, RIGHT HERE.

CALVIN and HOBBES

by WATTERSON

THIS IS SUPPOSED TO BE GREAT ART.

...SO WHY DOES IT LOOK LIKE A BUNCH OF DECAPITATED NAKED PEOPLE?

STRANGE FEELING [CO]MES OVER CALVIN [IN] THE ART MUSEUM.

HIS PARENTS, ENGROSSED IN CULTURE, REMAIN BLISSFULLY UNAWARE OF CALVIN'S TERRIBLE TRANSFORMATION!

YES, A TYRANNOSAURUS IS LOOSE IN THE ART MUSEUM! THE CURATOR SHRIEKS, AND PANDEMONIUM ENSUES!

A GUARD REACHES FOR HIS PISTOL, BUT THE DINOSAUR IS UPON HIM AND HE IS MESSILY DEVOURED!

[TH]E GIANT LIZARD'S GLORY IS CAP-[TU]RED FOREVER ON FILM BY THE [AN]TI-THEFT CAMERAS! PATRONS OF [TH]E ARTS FLEE FOR THEIR LIVES!

HUNDREDS OF PRICELESS PAINTINGS ARE RIPPED TO SHREDS IN THE AWFUL RAMPAGE! WEALTHY BENEFACTORS ARE TRAMPLED! THE MUSEUM IS IN RUINS! ON TO SYMPHONY HALL!!

CALVIN? ... CALVIN? WE'RE IN THE NEXT ROOM NOW. C'MON.

I THINK WE'D BETTER GET HIM OUT OF HERE. HE HAD THAT GRIN AGAIN.

I WANNA SEE THE DINOSAURS AT THE NATURAL HISTORY MUSEUM AGAIN.

WE SPENT ALL AFTERNOON THERE, CALVIN.

[Thi]s was an early tyrannosaur strip. The number of fingers, his alligator belly, the dragging tail, etc., are all wrong. Obviously, I did no research whatsoever. The parents [are] admiring a *Krazy Kat* landscape in the fourth panel.

Politics seems to be more and more poll driven, although I don't know that there's any connection between what we need and what we like. Calvin is not entirely clear on how his dad stays Dad, so he polls his own opinions and attempts to influence·policy with the statistics. By the way, I think there should be a statute of limitations on yearbook photographs.

Hobbes periodically gets washed in the washing machine. Calvin seems to take this in stride, but it's one of the stranger blurrings of what Hobbes is.

I imagine it must be a great temptation to misuse one's parental authority for private jokes.

Calvin's transmogrifier sums up the spirit of the strip. A cardboard box becomes a series of great inventions with a little imagination. The transmogrifier shows the kind of kid Calvin is, and it added a new dimension to the strip's world. This was an important story for *Calvin and Hobbes*, and I've used the transmogrifier several times since.

You can lead people to truth, but you can't make them understand it: the story of my youth, as seen from the present.

For several years, I had Calvin's family go camping for vacation. The stories are mostly invented, but they're based on memories of trips my family took when I was a kid. Dried food looks pretty good after scaling, beheading, and gutting a gasping fish.

Sunday strips must be drawn two months before publication to allow for color plates. To include a Sunday strip in a story, the entire story must be written that fa[r] advance, and I'm almost never that far ahead on daily strips. Also, some papers don't have Sunday editions or they don't buy the Sunday strip, so a Sunday installment c[an't] be crucial to the plot. For these reasons, it's rarely worth the trouble to coordinate Sundays and dailies.

WE'RE PACKING UP?

YEP. I'VE HAD ENOUGH. WHAT A ROTTEN WEEK!

WAP

DID YOU KNOW WHAT ANY OF DAD'S WORDS MEANT?

NO, BUT I WROTE THEM DOWN SO WE CAN LOOK 'EM UP WHEN WE GET HOME.

WELL, GANG, I'M SORRY THE WEATHER WASN'T ANY BETTER THIS WEEK.

I KNOW IT WASN'T ALWAYS A LOT OF FUN, BUT WE LIVED THROUGH IT, AND WE GOT TO SPEND SOME TIME TOGETHER, AND THAT'S WHAT'S REALLY IMPORTANT.

ANYWAY, I HOPE YOU'RE ALL NOT *TOO* DISAPPOINTED.

CALVIN, TELL YOUR DAD ANY JUDGE WOULD TAKE THIS TRIP AS GROUNDS FOR DIVORCE.

DAD, MOM SAYS...

ALL RIGHT! ALL RIGHT!

dad used to say this.

SPACEMAN SPIFF

Spaceman Spiff predates *Calvin and Hobbes* by over a decade. I trace Spiff back to a comic strip I drew for a high school German class, called *Raumfahrer Rolf*. It was a pretty silly two-page comic in which the protagonist got eaten by a monster at the end, but it was written in some sort of German, and that was what counted. I reworked the character in college, calling him "Spaceman Mort," but the strip was conceived as a fairly elaborate, continuing project and that didn't seem like the best use of my academic time, so I never published it.

A year or so after college, the newly christened *Spaceman Spiff* was my first strip submission to newspaper syndicates. Spiff was a diminutive loudmouth, not unlike Calvin, albeit with a Chaplin mustache, flying goggles, and a cigar. He had a dimwitted assistant named Fargle, and they roamed through space in a dirigible. For obvious reasons, the syndicates rejected it. Years later, when I came up with Calvin, I finally had the opportunity to bring Spiff back.

When I was a kid, I followed the Apollo moon program with great interest, so Calvin shares that fascination with space travel. Spaceman Spiff is also a bit of a spoof on *Flash Gordon*. The narration in *Flash Gordon* is fairly overwrought, so I have Spiff describe his own exploits with a similar search for breathless superlatives.

The Spiff strips are limited in narrative potential, but I keep doing them because they're so much fun to draw. The planets and monsters offer great visual possibilities, especially in the Sunday strips. Most of the alien landscapes come from the canyons and deserts of southern Utah, a place more weird and spectacular than anything I'd previously been able to make up. The landscapes have become a significant part of the Spaceman Spiff sequences, and I often write the strip around the topography I feel like drawing.

Like all of Calvin's fantasies, Spaceman Spiff provides a way for me to draw some other comic strip when I want a break from *Calvin and Hobbes*. I can draw and write things that wouldn't fit in the strip otherwise, and this opens up opportunities to experiment with new interests.

Calvin and Hobbes by WATTERSON

THE DREADED SCUM BEINGS FIRE! SPACEMAN SPIFF IS *HIT!*

IT NEVER FAILS. I JUST WASHED AND WAXED THIS THING.

UR HERO, THE INTREPID ACEMAN SPIFF, STRUGGLES TH THE CONTROLS OF HIS AMAGED SPACECRAFT!

THE FREEM PROPULSION BLASTERS ARE USELESS! SPIFF CRASHES ONTO THE SURFACE OF AN ALIEN PLANET!

UNSCATHED, THE FEARLESS SPACE EXPLORER EMERGES FROM THE SMOLDERING WRECKAGE! HE IS MAROONED ON A HOSTILE WORLD!

SCORCHED BY TWIN SUNS, THE PLANET IS NOTHING BUT BARREN ROCK AND METHANE! THERE'S NO HOPE OF FINDING FOOD OR WATER!

IFF COLLAPSES! OH NO, A EOUS ALIEN SPOTS HIM! IN WEAKENED STATE, SPIFF IS MATCH FOR THE MONSTER! *HIS COULD BE THE END!!*

LUNCHTIME! I BROUGHT YOU A SANDWICH AND SOME LEMONADE.

BRING THE DISHES BACK WHEN YOU'RE DONE, OK?

...OH WELL.

THANKS, MOM.

I overplayed the quasi-romantic tension between Calvin and Susie in early stories. This story was an improvement, because I just let the two personalities bounce off each other.

CALViN AND HOBBES by WATTERSON

First there was nothing...

...then there was Calvin!

Calvin, the mighty god, creates the universe with pure will!

From utter nothingness comes swirling form! Life begins where once was void!

But Calvin is no kind and loving god! He's one of the old gods! He demands sacrifice!

Yes, Calvin is a god of the underworld! And the puny inhabitants of earth displease him!

The great Calvin ignores their pleas for mercy and the doomed writhe in agony!

HAVE YOU SEEN HOW ABSORBED CALVIN IS WITH THOSE TINKERTOYS? HE'S CREATING WHOLE WORLDS OVER THERE!

I'LL BET HE GROWS UP TO BE AN ARCHITECT.

This is not a great strip, but it was made worse by the Sunday format restrictions. Several of the panel divisions are mandatory, so I was forced to waste space in some panels (especially the first) and cram too much into panels elsewhere. I'd been frustrated before, but this time the format ruined what I had in mind.

I regret introducing Uncle Max into the strip. At the time, I thought a new character related to the family would open up story possibilities: the family could go visit Max, and so on. After the story ran, I realized that I hadn't established much identity for Max, and that he didn't bring out anything new in Calvin. The character, I concluded, was redundant. It was also very awkward that Max could not address Calvin's parents by name, and this should have tipped me off that the strip was not designed for the parents to have outside adult relationships. Max is gone.

ral years ago, on a whim, I bought a model airplane and built it. It's as frustrating now as when I was a kid. I got a few strips out of it though. In this one, I like the nd panel "throwaway joke" more than the rest of the strip.

High on my list of adulthood pleasures is the fact that nobody makes me wrestle sweaty guys anymore.

I hope some historian will confirm that I was the first cartoonist to use the word "booger" in a newspaper comic strip.

I think we've all gone through something like this story. You die a thousand deaths before you even get in trouble.

HOBBES! YOU'VE GOT TO HELP ME! I'M IN BIG TROUBLE!

WHAT'S THE MATTER?

YOU KNOW HOW DAD SAID I COULD USE HIS BINOCULARS AS LONG AS I WAS EXTRA CAREFUL WITH THEM? WELL, I JUST BROKE THEM BY ACCIDENT!

NOW I NEED SOME ADVICE. SHOULD I RUN AWAY, OR COMMIT HARA-KIRI?

OVER THE BINOCULARS?

YEAH.

MAYBE BOTH.

GEEZ, I CAN'T BELIEVE I BROKE DAD'S BINOCULARS! HE'LL BLOW EVERY CAPILLARY IN HIS BODY!

DAD SAID I HAD TO BE VERY, VERY CAREFUL WITH THEM, AND WHAT DO I DO? I GO AND BREAK THEM. HE'LL FLAY ME ALIVE!

HOW DID YOU DO IT, ANYWAY?

I JUST DROPPED THEM.

AND THEY BROKE?

WELL, I WAS TOSSING THEM TO MYSELF AT THE TIME, AS I RAN DOWN THE SIDEWALK.

HOW MUCH MONEY DO YOU HAVE, HOBBES? MAYBE WE CAN BUY DAD A NEW PAIR OF BINOCULARS BEFORE HE GETS HOME.

I'VE GOT THIRTY...NO, THIRTY-FIVE CENTS.

GREAT. I'VE GOT FOUR DOLLARS. LET'S CALL THE STORE.

HELLO? I'D LIKE TO KNOW HOW MUCH A GOOD PAIR OF BINOCULARS COSTS.

ONE TO SIX HUNDRED DOLLARS?! DO YOU HAVE ANY IDEA WHAT MY DAD'S GOING TO *DO* TO ME?!?

HE WON'T STOP AT KILLING YOU, THAT'S FOR SURE. UH *UH*.

I HAD NO *IDEA* BINOCULARS WERE SO EXPENSIVE! WE'RE DOOMED! WE'RE DOOMED!

"WE"?

WHY IN THE WORLD DID DAD LET ME USE ANYTHING SO VALUABLE?! HE SHOULD'VE *KNOWN* I'D BREAK THEM! HE MUST'VE BEEN OUT OF HIS MIND! THIS IS ALL *HIS* FAULT!

WHAT AM I GONNA *DO*.?

I SUPPOSE YOU *COULD* JUST TELL HIM WHAT HAPPENED...

..AND MAKE MY GETAWAY WHEN THE CORONARY HITS? SAY, *THAT'S* AN IDEA!

I've never understood people who remember childhood as an idyllic time.

I think this is one of the better Rosalyn stories. With each one, it gets harder to top the previous conflict, so this time I added Stupendous Man to the mix.

WHAT ARE WE GOING TO *DO*, HOBBES? ROSALYN WILL BE HERE IN JUST A FEW HOURS!

DO YOU THINK SHE'LL REMEMBER HOW YOU LOCKED HER OUTSIDE LAST TIME?

IF SHE DOES, WE'RE DEAD! SHE'LL PROBABLY STICK MY HEAD ON A STAKE IN THE FRONT YARD AS A WARNING TO *OTHER* KIDS SHE BABY-SITS!

I'M ALMOST SURE THAT WOULD VIOLATE SOME ZONING ORDINANCE.

WELL NO MATTER WHAT, WE'RE IN BIG TROUBLE UNLESS WE THINK OF SOMETHING *FAST!*

I SUPPOSE WE COULD TRY BEING *GOOD*.

I MUST'VE GOTTEN WATER IN MY EAR. *WHAT* DID YOU SAY?

NOTHING. FORGET IT.

HI ROSALYN, COME ON IN. THANKS FOR COMING AGAIN.

NO TROUBLE.

HI ROSALYN! YOU DON'T NEED TO WORRY *THIS* TIME. CALVIN WILL BE ON HIS BEST BEHAVIOR TONIGHT.

EVEN SO, I'D LIKE AN ADVANCE.

AN ADVANCE? BUT... BUT...

DEAR, MAY I SPEAK WITH YOU A MOMENT?

BUT WE *GAVE* HER AN ADVANCE ON TONIGHT WHEN SHE *LEFT* LAST TIME!

I DON'T CARE. JUST PAY WHAT IT TAKES TO GET US OUT OF HERE!

A BOLT OF FIERY CRIMSON STREAKS ACROSS THE SKY! IT'S *STUPENDOUS MAN!*

THE FIENDISH *BABY SITTER GIRL* HAS A LOCAL HOUSEHOLD IN HER IRON GRIP OF TERROR! THE MAN OF MEGA-MIGHT ZOOMS TO THE RESCUE!

I'M IN LUCK! BABY SITTER GIRL IS MOMENTARILY DISTRACTED!

HI CHARLIE, IT'S ROSALYN. YEAH, I'M OVER AT THE LITTLE MONSTER'S HOUSE AGAIN. HMM? NO, ACTUALLY HE'S BEEN PRETTY GOOD TONIGHT. YEAH, I CAN'T BELIEVE IT.

ANYWAY CHARLIE, I'M SORRY WE COULDN'T GO OUT TONIGHT, BUT THIS LITTLE CREEP'S PARENTS ARE SO DESPERATE TO GET AWAY FROM HIM ONCE IN A WHILE THAT THEY...

YAHH! FREEDOM AND JUSTICE SHALL ALWAYS PREVAIL OVER TYRANNY, BABY SITTER GIRL!

GET OFF ME, CALVIN, YOU PEST! OW! LET GO! QUIT IT!

STUPENDOUS MAN HAS THE STRENGTH OF A MILLION MORTAL MEN! GIVE UP!

LISTEN CHARLIE, I'M GOING TO HAVE TO CALL YOU BACK. YOU WOULDN'T BELIEVE WHAT THIS CRETIN IS WEARING.

WITH MUSCLES OF MAGNITUDE, *STUPENDOUS MAN* FIGHTS WITH HEROIC RESOLVE!

THERE IS NO WAY I'M GETTING PAID ENOUGH FOR THIS KIND OF AGGRAVATION. HOW COULD A KID WITH SUCH LITTLE LEGS GO SO FAST?!

SECURE IN HIS SECRET FORTRESS, **STUPENDOUS MAN** PLANS HIS STRATEGY! BABY SITTER GIRL IS NO MATCH FOR **STUPENDOUS MAN'S** STUPENDOUS INTELLECT!

CALVIN, YOU'RE IN BIG TROUBLE IF YOU DON'T COME OUT!

YOU MADE IT BACK ALIVE!

OF COURSE! I MADE A STUPENDOUS DASH AS SOON AS ROSALYN WENT AROUND THE HOUSE! SHE *STILL* DOESN'T KNOW WHERE I AM!

THERE GOES ROSALYN AROUND THE HOUSE AGAIN. SHE STILL DOESN'T KNOW YOU SNEAKED BACK INSIDE.

NOW I'LL CHANGE BACK INTO MY SECRET IDENTITY ALTER EGO!

UH OH. SHE SAW THE LIGHT ON IN THIS ROOM. SHE'S COMING IN!

QUICK! GET IN THE COVERS! PRETEND WE'VE JUST BEEN READING IN BED!

BUT SHE KNOWS YOU ATTACKED HER AND RAN OUTSIDE HALF AN HOUR AGO!

THAT WAS **STUPENDOUS MAN**, NOT MILD-MANNERED CALVIN! *I'VE* BEEN IN BED WITH MY PJs ON SINCE 8:00.

YOU THINK SHE'S GOING TO BELIEVE *THAT?*

MY COVERS ARE HERE. MY PAJAMAS ARE *HERE.* IT'S AS PLAIN AS CAN BE!

ALL RIGHT! I FOUND YOU!

FOUND?? WHY, WHAT DO YOU MEAN? I'VE BEEN IN BED READING ALL EVENING WITH HOBBES.

DON'T GIVE ME THAT! YOU JUST NOW SNEAKED INSIDE, TOOK OFF YOUR SILLY COSTUME, AND JUMPED IN BED! I KNOW WHAT YOU DID! WELL YOU'RE GONNA GET IT *NOW*, BUCKO!

OH YEAH? WHAT ARE YOU GOING TO DO TO ME, HUH? YOU CAN'T SEND ME TO BED WHEN I'M ALREADY *IN* BED! SORRY TO SPOIL YOUR FUN, YOU EEL!

OK, DOWNSTAIRS! *MARCH!*

HEY, YOU CAN'T TAKE ME *OUT* OF BED! I NEED MY *SLEEP!* HEY! HEY!

WHILE YOUR DAD IS TAKING ROSALYN HOME, PERHAPS *YOU'D* LIKE TO EXPLAIN WHAT HAPPENED TONIGHT.

GOSH MOM, WHAT'S TO TELL? AT 8:00, I PUT ON MY PAJAMAS, BRUSHED MY TEETH AND WENT STRAIGHT TO BED. NOTHING HAPPENED.

AND THIS?

UH... *LIES!* ALL LIES! ROSALYN MADE ME DO THAT JUST SO I'D GET IN TROUBLE! SHE HATES KIDS! NONE OF THAT IS TRUE! I WENT STRAIGHT TO BED!

NICE TRY, PINOCCHIO.

WELL WHO WOULD'VE THOUGHT ROSALYN WOULD MAKE ME WRITE A FULL CONFESSION?!

The strips of these two pages are part of a story where Calvin goes to Mars. It was an early attempt to write something with an environmental message, and the story was pretty heavy-handed. The cartoony backgrounds are a bit overdone too. Working on deadline, I have to go with story ideas as they come, but this one needed a few more rewrites.

I got some nasty mail about this strip. Some readers thought it was inexcusable to show a kid fantasize about bombing his school off the face of the earth. Apparently some of my readers were never kids themselves.

Calvin is a great character to write for, because I only need to know as much as a lazy six-year-old. After this story ran, I received more information on bats than I ever cared to know.

I'VE GOT TO WRITE A REPORT FOR SCHOOL.

WHAT'S YOUR TOPIC?

BATS. CAN YOU IMAGINE ANYTHING MORE STUPID?

HECK, *I* DON'T KNOW ANYTHING ABOUT BATS! HOW AM I SUPPOSED TO WRITE A REPORT ON A SUBJECT I KNOW NOTHING ABOUT?! IT'S IMPOSSIBLE!

I SUPPOSE RESEARCH IS OUT OF THE QUESTION.

OH, LIKE I'M GOING TO LEARN ABOUT BATS AND *THEN* WRITE A REPORT?! GIVE ME A BREAK!

HELLO, SUSIE? THIS IS CALVIN. YOU KNOW THIS REPORT WE'RE SUPPOSED TO WRITE FOR SCHOOL? YEAH. MY TOPIC IS BATS. WHAT'S YOURS?

ELEPHANTS? HMM. WELL, ARE YOU GOING TO THE LIBRARY TO LOOK UP ELEPHANTS? YOU ARE? GREAT!

WHILE YOU'RE THERE, COULD YOU RESEARCH BATS TOO, AND MAKE COPIES OF ALL THE INFORMATION YOU FIND, AND MAYBE UNDERLINE THE IMPORTANT PARTS FOR ME, AND SORT OF OUTLINE IT, SO I WOULDN'T HAVE TO READ IT ALL?

HOW'D IT GO?

I REALLY LOATHE GIRLS.

CALVIN and HOBBES

by WATTERSON

UH-O...

OH NO! EVERYTHING HAS SUDDENLY TURNED NEO-CUBIST!

IT ALL STARTED WHEN CALVIN ENGAGED HIS DAD IN A MINOR DEBATE! SOON CALVIN COULD SEE BOTH SIDES OF THE ISSUE! THEN POOR CALVIN BEGAN TO SEE BOTH SIDES OF *EVERY*THING!

TRADITIONAL SINGLE VIEWPOINT BEEN ABANDONED! PERSPECTIVE HAS BEEN FRACTURED!

THE MULTIPLE VIEWS PROVIDE TOO MUCH INFORMATION! IT'S IMPOSSIBLE TO MOVE! CALVIN QUICKLY TRIES TO ELIMINATE ALL BUT ONE PERSPECTIVE!

IT WORKS! THE WORLD FALLS INTO A RECOGNIZABLE ORDER!

YOU'RE STILL WRONG, DAD.

ften paralyzed by being able to see all sides of an issue. I worked that into my interest in art for this strip, which was a lot of fun to draw.

This is part of a story where Calvin keeps getting bigger. At this point, I stopped trying to put in humorous dialogue, and just let the pictures advance the plot. My original idea was to do this for a month and see how long readers would put up with it. I wisely chickened out, since the idea wasn't all that interesting to begin with. It's just weird for weirdness's sake, and I don't think it holds up very well.

This strip got *Calvin and Hobbes* canceled from one newspaper. The paper had just picked up the strip when this example of disgusting juvenile humor appeared. Generally, I've been able to keep Calvin in newspapers longer than a week, but not this time.

Pen and ink is not a great medium for suggesting atmospherics, but the second panel here works pretty well. Waiting for the bus in bad weather, whether going to school or a job, always seemed like adding insult to injury. Rainy days should be spent at home with a cup of tea and a good book.

The illusion of control.

Most cartoon characters have a generic white collar job, but eventually I decided that Calvin's dad, like my dad, is a patent attorney. I think it's funnier when things are specific, rather than generalized.

CALVIN'S WAGON

Calvin's wagon is a simple device to add some physical comedy to the strip, and I most often use it when Calvin gets longwinded or philosophical. I think the action lends a silly counterpoint to the text, and it's a lot more interesting to draw than talking heads. Sometimes the wagon ride even acts as a visual metaphor for Calvin's topic of discussion.

Calvin rides the wagon through the woods, bouncing off rocks and flying over ravines. When I was a kid, our backyard dropped off into a big woods, but it was brambly and swampy, not like Calvin's, which seems to be more like a national forest. I was not a real outdoorsy kid, but occasionally I'd tramp out through the brush to map a pond, or to try to see unusual birds and animals. Calvin's woods is important to the strip, because it's the place where Calvin and Hobbes can get away from everyone and be themselves. The solitude of the woods brings out Calvin's small, but redeeming, contemplative side.

For some reason, when I watch my cats sleep, poems spring to mind.

STILL AND QUIET FELINE FORM,
IN THE SUN, ASLEEP AND WARM.
HIS TAIL IS LIMP, HIS
WHISKERS DROOPED.
MAN, WHAT COULD MAKE
THIS CAT SO POOPED?

SHEESHH..

MY TIGER, IT SEEMS, IS RUNNING 'ROUND NUDE.
THIS FUR COAT MUST HAVE MADE HIM PERSPIRE.
IT LIES ON THE FLOOR - SHOULD THIS BE CONSTRUED
AS A PERMANENT CHANGE OF ATTIRE?
PERHAPS HE CONSIDERS ITS COLORS PASSÉ,
OR MAYBE IT FIT HIM TOO SNUG
WILL HE WANT IT BACK? SHOULD I PUT IT AWAY?
OR USE IT RIGHT HERE AS A RUG?

I WONDER WHEN
SCHOOL STARTS.

My dad and I still have this relationship, but I like to think I go a little easier on my mom now.

WELL, LOOK WHO'S UP! GOOD MORNING SLEEPYHEAD!

YOU'VE MISSED THE BEST PART OF THE DAY! I'VE BEEN UP SINCE 6:30 GETTING MANY THINGS ACCOMPLISHED!

AT LEAST WHEN I HAVE A DAY OFF, I CAN TELL THE DIFFERENCE.

I JUST *KNOW* SOME NURSE SWITCHED THE BASSINETS.

HERE'S SOME CLEAN CLOTHES. WILL YOU PUT THEM AWAY PLEASE?

HEY, MY UNDERWEAR ISN'T PRESSED! NEITHER ARE MY SOCKS! YOU DIDN'T FINISH IRONING!

BUDDY, IF YOU WANT YOUR UNDERWEAR IRONED, YOU CAN DO IT YOURSELF!

WHAT KIND OF MOTHER *ARE* YOU?!

SHE SHOULD TAKE MORE PRIDE IN HER WORK.

I never write stories with the ending in mind, because I want the story to develop a life of its own, and I want the resolution of the dilemma to surprise me. Sometimes I really get myself stuck that way. This story spun completely out of control and surprised me throughout, so it's one of my favorites. I think most of us would be horrified to meet ourselves and discover what everyone else already knows about us.

OK DUPLICATES, LISTEN UP. AS LONG AS YOU'RE ALL HERE AND I DON'T KNOW HOW TO GET RID OF YOU, WE MIGHT AS WELL COOPERATE.

SPECIFICALLY, WITH FIVE DUPLICATES, WE CAN DIVIDE UP THE SCHOOL WEEK SO THERE'S ONE DUPLICATE FOR EACH DAY.

IF THE REST OF US LAY LOW, WE CAN TAKE TURNS GOING TO SCHOOL, AND NO ONE WILL BE THE WISER!

GREAT!

NOW THAT STILL LEAVES US WITH THE QUESTION OF WHO GETS THE BED TONIGHT.

WE'LL FIGHT YOU FOR IT.

HI CALVIN.

I'M NOT CALVIN. I'M DUPLICATE NUMBER TWO.

WHAT ARE YOU TALKING ABOUT?

WE DREW STRAWS, AND TODAY'S MY DAY TO GO TO SCHOOL. WE'RE ALL TAKING TURNS SO WE EACH ONLY GO ONCE A WEEK.

CALVIN, YOU ARE SO WEIRD I'M NOT EVEN GOING TO TALK TO YOU.

I'M NOT CALVIN.

I WISH I LIVED SOMEPLACE WHERE I WENT TO A NORMAL BUS STOP.

ARE YOU IN CALVIN'S CLASS? WILL YOU HELP ME FIND HIS LOCKER?

CALVIN, WOULD YOU PLEASE DEMONSTRATE THE HOMEWORK PROBLEM YOU WERE ASSIGNED YESTERDAY?

I WASN'T HERE YESTERDAY.

YES, YOU WERE, CALVIN. DIDN'T YOU DO YOUR PROBLEM?

I'M NOT CALVIN. I'M DUPLICATE NUMBER FIVE. DUPLICATE *TWO* WAS HERE YESTERDAY, NOT *ME*. WE'RE ALL TAKING TURNS. NUMBER TWO WILL BE BACK NEXT WEEK, AND YOU CAN ASK HIM TO DO THE PROBLEM *THEN*.

LOOK, I DON'T SEE WHAT'S SO HARD ABOUT THIS!

PRINCIPAL

GUYS? IT'S OK TO COME OUT! IT'S ME, NUMBER FOUR. I'M HOME.

HOW WAS SCHOOL TODAY?

AHH, I GOT SENT TO THE PRINCIPAL'S OFFICE, JUST LIKE NUMBERS TWO AND FIVE DID.

GEEZ, YOU GUYS! EVEN *I* DON'T GET SENT TO THE PRINCIPAL EVERY *DAY!* YOU'RE MAKING ME LOOK BAD!

LOOK, CALVIN, IF YOU DON'T LIKE OUR PERFORMANCE YOU CAN GO TO SCHOOL *YOURSELF!*

WHOA, LET'S NOT JUMP TO CONCLUSIONS! I'M JUST SAYING THERE'S ROOM FOR IMPROVEMENT.

HEY FOUR, WERE YOU ABLE TO SWIPE ANY CHALK?

YEAH! THE PRINCIPAL NEVER FRISKED ME!

CALVIN and HOBBES
by WATTERSON

AHHHH...

UH-OH. SOMETHING IS SERIOUSLY WRONG HERE.

THE LAWS OF PERSPECTIVE HAVE BEEN REPEALED!

OBJECTS NO LONGER DIMINISH IN SIZE WITH DISTANCE!

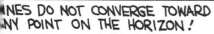

LINES DO NOT CONVERGE TOWARD ANY POINT ON THE HORIZON!

ALL SPATIAL RELATIONSHIPS ARE LOST! IT'S IMPOSSIBLE TO JUDGE WHERE ANYTHING IS! OH NO!

CALVIN, QUIT RUNNING AROUND AND CRASHING INTO THINGS, OR I'LL SELL YOU TO THE MONKEY HOUSE!

...AND NOW *SHE'S* LOST PERSPECTIVE.

is strip was a lot of fun to draw. It was surprising how often I had to "correct" the perspective to make it wrong.

Much of this story is based on actual memories, and I think it nicely touches on a number of issues. I still have no use for organized sports of any kind. This story also introduced Calvinball, another idea that captures the spirit of the strip.

I SIGNED UP TO PLAY BASEBALL EVERY RECESS, AND I DON'T EVEN *LIKE* BASEBALL THAT MUCH.

I MEAN, IT'S FUN PLAYING BASEBALL WITH JUST *YOU*, BECAUSE WE BOTH GET TO PITCH, BAT, RUN AND CATCH ALL AT ONCE. WE GET TO *DO* EVERYTHING.

MOSTLY WE JUST ARGUE OVER THE RULES WE MAKE UP! THAT'S THE PART *I* LIKE!

BUT THIS WILL BE WITH *TEAMS* AND ASSIGNED POSITIONS AND AN UMPIRE! IT'S *BORING* PLAYING IT THE *REAL* WAY!

DO YOU EVEN KNOW *HOW* TO PLAY THE REAL WAY?

SEE, THAT'S *ANOTHER* PROBLEM! SUPPOSE THEY MAKE ME A HALFBACK. CAN I TACKLE THE SHORTSTOP OR NOT?

I HEAR YOU SIGNED UP TO PLAY SOFTBALL AT RECESS.

YEAH, BUT I DIDN'T EVEN WANT TO. I JUST DID IT TO STOP GETTING TEASED.

WELL, SPORTS ARE GOOD FOR YOU. THEY TEACH TEAMWORK AND COOPERATION. YOU LEARN HOW TO WIN GRACIOUSLY AND ACCEPT DEFEAT. IT BUILDS CHARACTER.

EVERY TIME I'VE BUILT CHARACTER, I'VE REGRETTED IT! I DON'T *WANT* TO LEARN TEAMWORK! I DON'T *WANT* TO LEARN ABOUT WINNING AND LOSING! HECK, I DON'T EVEN WANT TO *COMPETE*! WHAT'S WRONG WITH JUST HAVING FUN BY YOURSELF, HUH?!

WHEN YOU GROW UP, IT'S NOT ALLOWED.

ALL THE MORE REASON I SHOULD DO IT *NOW*!

128

CALVIN and HObbES
by WATTERSON

OLLY-WOLLY POLLIWOGGY UMP-BUMP FIZZ!

HEY!

HA! TOLE UR AG!

BUT I HIT YOU WITH THE CALVIN BALL! YOU HAVE TO PUT THE FLAG BACK AND SING THE "I'M VERY SORRY" SONG!

I DON'T HAVE TO SING THE SONG! I WAS IN THE "NO SONG" ZONE!

NO YOU WEREN'T. I TOUCHED THE "OPPOSITE POLE", SO THE "NO SONG ZONE" IS NOW A "SONG ZONE"!

I DIDN'T SEE YOU TOUCH THE OPPOSITE POLE! YOU HAVE TO DECLARE IT!

I DECLARED IT OPPOSITELY BY *NOT* DECLARING IT. START SINGING.

"HERE'S THE 'VERY SORRY SONGG'. WON'T YOU HELP AND SING ALONGG?"

BUM BUM BUM

BLEW IT! ..... HE'S SORRY!
KNEW IT! ..... SO SORRY!
VERY VERY   JUST DON'T DO IT
RY THAT I   ANY MORE, YOU
K YOUR   SCURVY
CIOUS FLAAGGG! SCALAWAAGGG!

I'M FREE! I GET FREE PASSAGE TO WICKET FIVE!

NO, THAT'S WHAT WE DID LAST TIME, REMEMBER?

OH YEAH. HMM.

OK, THE *NEW* RULE IS WE HAVE TO JUMP EVERYWHERE UNTIL SOMEONE FINDS THE BONUS BOX!

THAT'S GOOD!

THE ONLY PERMANENT RULE IN CALVINBALL IS THAT YOU CAN'T PLAY IT THE SAME WAY TWICE!

THE SCORE IS STILL Q TO 12!

le have asked how to play Calvinball. It's pretty simple: you make up the rules as you go.

Calvin's parents are sometimes ambivalent about their child's effect on their lives, as I imagine any sane parent would be. Depicting that used to disturb some readers, who expected family strips to be highly sanitized. Now that television sitcoms are commonly a half-hour volley of vicious insults, this sort of strip looks positively heartwarming.

Calvin and Hobbes
by WATTERSON

TOAD STROGANOFF!

..EWWWW..

POKE POKE

AUGH!

CLINK
CLINK
CLINK

HA!

SPLORPP!

SPLAT!

DON'T BLAME ME. I'M THE ONE WHO SAID WE SHOULD CALL FOR A PIZZA.

en I was a kid, I drew a comic strip about oatmeal that was alive. At the time, I thought that was absolutely hilarious, so I suppose that's where this es from. Calvin's adversarial relationship with his mom's cooking is a slight exaggeration of my own fussy eating habits as a kid.

Tracer Bullet stories are extremely time-consuming to write, so I don't attempt them often. I'm not at all familiar with *film noir* or detective novels, so these are just spoofs on the clichés of the genre. Cartoonists don't use black much anymore (the eye, being lazy, is attracted to empty white space, especially when the panels are so small), and we miss some dramatic possibilities that way.

THE DAME SAID SHE HAD A CASE. SHE SOUNDED LIKE A CASE HERSELF, BUT I CAN'T CHOOSE MY CLIENTS.

SHE WAS THE PUSHY TYPE. THE KIND WHO'D BREAK YOUR HEART, OR MAYBE YOUR ARMS. I HURRIED OVER.

EITHER SHE HAD A PSYCHOTIC DECORATOR, OR HER PLACE HAD BEEN RANSACKED BY SOMEONE IN A BIG HURRY.

WELL?! HOW DO YOU EXPLAIN THIS?

THE DAME WAS HYSTERICAL. DAMES USUALLY ARE.

WHAT HAVE YOU GOT TO SAY FOR YOURSELF?

DON'T TOUCH ANYTHING. I'M LOOKING FOR CLUES.

THE CLICK OF A HAMMER BEING COCKED BEHIND MY HEAD FOCUSED MY THOUGHTS LIKE ONLY A LOADED .38 CAN.

THE DAME HAD SET ME UP! SHE DIDN'T WANT ME TO SOLVE THE CASE AT ALL! SHE JUST WANTED A PATSY TO PIN THE CRIME ON!

WELL?

I DIDN'T LIKE THE WAY THIS STORY WAS SHAPING UP, SO I DECIDED TO WRITE A NEW ENDING WITH MY .45 AUTOMATIC AS CO-AUTHOR.

I INTRODUCED THE DAME TO A FRIEND WHO'S VERY CLOSE TO MY HEART. JUST A LITTLE DOWN AND LEFT, TO BE SPECIFIC.

MY FRIEND IS AN ELOQUENT SPEAKER. HE MADE THREE PROFOUND ARGUMENTS WHILE I EXCUSED MYSELF FROM THE ROOM. I ALWAYS LEAVE WHEN THE TALK GETS PHILOSOPHICAL.

YOU'RE IN *REAL* TROUBLE NOW, YOUNG MAN !!

I'D JUST FINISHED PUTTING THE PUZZLE PIECES TOGETHER WHEN THE DAME'S HIRED GOON JUMPED OUT OF NOWHERE AND PRACTICED FOR HIS CHIROPRACTIC DEGREE.

WHEN HE WAS DONE, AN ALL-PERCUSSION SYMPHONY WAS PLAYING IN MY HEAD, AND THE ACOUSTICS WERE INCREDIBLE. THE ORCHESTRA WENT ON A TEN-CITY TOUR OF MY BRAIN, AND I HAD A SEASON PASS WITH FRONT ROW SEATS.

I HAD FIGURED OUT WHO TRASHED THE DAME'S LIVING ROOM, BUT SINCE SHE WASN'T MY CLIENT ANY MORE, I FELT NO NEED TO DIVULGE THE INFORMATION.

BESIDES, THE CULPRIT HAPPENED TO BE A BUDDY OF MINE. I CLOSED THE CASE.

I GUESS WE SHOULD'VE PLAYED OUTSIDE, HUH?

CALVIN AND HObbES

by WATTERSON

WELL! PEANUT BUTTER!

...OR SO IT *SEEMS*.

HMM? WHAT?

MY SANDWICH WIGGLED! THERE'S SOMETHING *ALIVE* IN IT!

OH STOP IT, CALVIN.

I'M NOT KIDDING! MOM MUST BE TRYING TO KILL ME! I BET THERE'S A SLUG IN MY PEANUT BUTTER!

EWW!

HMM... I DON'T *FEEL* ANY SLUGS IN HERE. WHAT COULD IT BE? I'D BETTER SMELL IT.

AUGH! AUGH! IT'S GOT MY NOSE!! THE PEANUT BUTTER *ITSELF* IS ALIVE!

IT'S OOZING UP MY FACE! IT'S GOING TO SUCK OUT MY EYEBALLS! *HELP!*

RGH! MMF! BLRGHGH!

I GOT IT OFF! QUICK! DROWN IT IN CHOCOLATE MILK!

BOY, WHAT A CLOSE CALL *THAT* WAS! WON'T MOM BE DISAPPOINTED TO SEE HER LITTLE PLOT *FAILED!*

LOOK AT YOU! I'VE NEVER *SEEN* ANYTHING SO REVOLTING! WHAT'S WRONG WITH YOU?!

I'M EATING SOMEWHERE ELSE.

GIRLS ARE SO WEIRD.

will probably have trouble getting dates when he's older.

The Get Rid Of Slimy girlS club is based on similar clubs my next-door neighbor and I formed when we were kids. Our mission was to harass neighborhood girls, but if they wouldn't come out, we'd often settle for harassing my brother. We prepared for a lot of great struggles that never happened. Once we gathered big hickory nuts, loaded them into a suitcase, locked it so nobody else could open it, and stashed it up high in a tree. When the Critical Moment came, we planned to scramble up the tree and unleash a hail of nuts upon our astonished pursuers. Six months later, when the leaves were down, we looked up and discovered the suitcase was still in the tree. The hinges had rusted, the nuts had rotted, and the suitcase was ruined. Our great plans often had this kind of boring anticlimax, which is why fiction comes in so handy.

WE MADE IT TO SUSIE'S YARD!

BUT WHERE'S SUSIE? I DON'T SEE HER!

ARGHH! WE GO TO ALL THIS TROUBLE TO LAUNCH AN ATTACK ON HER, AND WHAT DOES SHE DO? SHE **MOVES**! ALL OUR GREAT PLANS ARE FOR NAUGHT! A WHOLE MORNING RUINED!

MAYBE SHE JUST WENT IN FOR LUNCH. SEE, SHE LEFT SOME OF HER TOYS OUT, SO SHE'S PROBABLY PLANNING TO COME BACK.

THAT GIVES ME A *FABULOUS* IDEA!

UH OH.

WHAT ARE YOU DOING? THAT'S SUSIE'S DOLL.

I KNOW. C'MON, LET'S SCRAM.

WE CAN'T TAKE HER DOLL! THAT WOULD BE *STEALING*!

NO IT WOULDN'T.

ARE WE GOING TO GIVE IT BACK?

IF SHE PAYS THE RANSOM!

WELL, THIS IS CERTAINLY A SORRY CHAPTER IN G.R.O.S.S. HISTORY! FIRST TIGER HOBBES, A TRAITOR TO THE CAUSE!

IT MIGHT INTEREST YOU TO KNOW THAT AFTER I WON SUSIE'S CONFIDENCE, I DID SOME SPYING.

SPYING? YOU WERE A SPY??

I READ AN OPEN PAGE OF SUSIE'S DIARY.

WOW! DEEP IN ENEMY TERRITORY, YOU INTERCEPTED A SECRET MESSAGE? WHAT DID IT SAY??

IT SAID, "CALVIN IS A PIG-FACED SMELLY FAT-HEAD!"

THEN OUR CLUB IS A SUCCESS! BRILLIANT WORK, HOBBES! PROMOTIONS FOR EVERYONE! WELCOME BACK!

CALVIN and HOBBES
by WATTERSON

THAT'S OUR SON! *SIGHH*

THESE PICT WILL REMI OF MORE WE WANT REMEMB

Standing in front of the mirror to sketch in this strip, I was glad I work in the privacy of my own home.

During my fight to keep the syndicate from licensing my work, I sometimes drew strips that had additional private meanings for myself. The cartoon above mocked my ability to argue with the syndicate, and the cartoon below is how I interpreted the syndicate's position. I wouldn't have drawn these if the material didn't stand on its own, or if it was in any way inconsistent with the characters, but cartoons such as these helped me laugh at my predicament at a time when very little about it seemed funny.

CALVIN AND HOBBES

by WATTERSON

CALVIN SUDDENLY REALIZES THE WORLD HAS NO HUE, VALUE, OR CHROMA!

HAVE THE PHOTORECEPTOR IN CALVIN'S EYES STOPPED WORKING PROPERLY, OR HAS THE FUNDAMENTAL NATURE OF LIGHT CHANGED??

PERHAPS SOME STRANGE NUCLEAR OR CHEMICAL REACTION ON THE SUN HAS CAUSED ELECTROMAGNETIC RADIATION TO DEFY SEPARATION INTO A SPECTRUM!

MAYBE OBJECTS NO LONGER REFLECT CERTAIN WAVELENGTHS! WHATEVER THE CAUSE, IT'S CLEAR TO CALVIN THAT THERE'S NO POINT IN DISCUSSING THINGS WITH HIS DAD!

THE PROBLEM IS, YOU SEE EVERYTHING IN TERMS OF BLACK AND WHITE.

SOMET THAT'S WAY T ARE

During the licensing fight, I was often accused of seeing issues in black and white, so I illustrated it literally for the strip. Calvin's retort is my own. It
challenge to make the pictures intelligible without any outlines. Best of all, I only needed to color one panel.

Sprite was often a model for Hobbes, both in looks and personality. When she died, I drew this cartoon. We can always meet again in dreams.

DINOSAURS

The dinosaurs I put in *Calvin and Hobbes* have become one of my favorite additions to the strip. Dinosaurs have appeared in many strips before mine, but I like to think I've treated them with a little more respect than they've often received at the hands of cartoonists.

When I was Calvin's age, I had a nicely illustrated dinosaur book and some dinosaur models, so it was a natural step to have Calvin share that interest. The first dinosaurs I put in the strip were based on my childhood memories of them. Back in the '60s, dinosaurs were imagined as lumbering, dim-witted, cold-blooded, oversized lizards. That's how I drew them in the first strips, and these drawings are now pretty embarrassing to look at. When I realized that dinosaurs offered Calvin interesting story possibilities, I started searching for books to rekindle my interest in them. It was then I discovered what I'd missed in paleontology during the last twenty years.

Dinosaurs, I quickly learned, were wilder than anything I'd ever imagined. Tails up, with birdlike agility, these were truly the creatures of nightmares. My drawings began to reflect the new information, and with each strip, I've tried to learn more and to depict dinosaurs more accurately. I do this partly for my own amusement, and partly because, for Calvin, dinosaurs are very, very real.

Dinosaurs have expanded Calvin's world and opened up some exciting graphic possibilities. The biggest reward for me, however, has been the fun I've had exploring a new interest. I enjoy dinosaurs more now than I did as a kid, and much of the job of being a cartoonist lies in keeping alive a sense of curiosity and wonder. Sometimes the best way to generate new ideas is to go out and learn something.

Calvin and Hobbes
by WATTERSON

GRGHHG

GHHHH

RRGHH

RGGHH
SNORRT
GHACKHGG

HEH HEH HEH
...SORRY...
..A LITTLE SINUS
CONGESTION...

SIGHHH..

Here is another story with Calvin and his cardboard box. Unlike most stories I write, this one creates some suspense at the beginning by dropping the reader into events without explaining what's going on. The humor of this story depends on the reader being familiar with Calvin's personality, so I could only do this sort of thing after the strip was established. Writing is most fun after readers are willing to enter the strip's world on its own terms.

I HEARD CALVIN SPLASHING IN THE TUB, BUT THERE'S NO WATER ON THE FLOOR.

HIS TOWEL IS HUNG TO DRY! THE TOOTHPASTE CAP IS ON! THERE'S NO MESS ANYWHERE!

AND YOU'RE ALREADY IN BED??

WOULD YOU CHECK OVER MY HOMEWORK TONIGHT, SO I CAN CORRECT ANY MISTAKES IN THE MORNING BEFORE SCHOOL? THANKS, MOM.

GOOD MORNING, MOM.

YOU'RE UP AND DRESSED?! I DIDN'T EVEN CALL YOU!

I LIKE TO GET UP EARLY SO THE MORNING ISN'T RUSHED.

AND WITH THE EXTRA TIME, I CAN REVIEW MY ASSIGNMENTS AND BE BETTER PREPARED FOR CLASS.

I'M BRACING MYSELF FOR WHEN THE OTHER SHOE DROPS.

DON'T GET UP. I'LL FIX MY OWN BREAKFAST. DO WE HAVE ANY PRUNES?

LAST TIME YOU MADE A DUPLICATE OF YOURSELF, THE *DUPLICATE* MADE DUPLICATES, REMEMBER? IT WAS A MESS!

TRUE, BUT THANKS TO THE ETHICATOR, IT CAN'T HAPPEN *THIS* TIME!

BY ONLY DUPLICATING MY *GOOD* SIDE, I'VE ENSURED THAT *THIS* DUPLICATE WON'T CAUSE ANY TROUBLE! HE'S A COMPLETE BOY SCOUT!

THERE'S NOTHING THIS TWERP LIKES BETTER THAN MAKING EVERYONE'S LIFE EASIER! HE LIVES FOR IT!

THE ETHICATOR MUST'VE DONE SOME DEEP DIGGING TO UNEARTH *HIM*!

TALK ABOUT SOMEONE EASY TO EXPLOIT!

WHEN YOU'RE DONE PUTTING MY TOYS AWAY, YOU CAN GET TO WORK ON MY MATH ASSIGNMENT.

OK.

ISN'T THIS THE LIFE? WE GET TO DO WHATEVER WE WANT WHILE GOODY-TWO-SHOES HERE DOES ALL THE WORK! HE DOESN'T EVEN COMPLAIN!

VIRTUE IS ITS OWN REWARD.

HE DOESN'T COMPLAIN, BUT HIS SELF-RIGHTEOUSNESS SURE GETS ON MY NERVES.

I HEAR YOU'RE PRETTY SMOOTH WITH THE LADIES! WOO WOO WOO!

OH, KNOCK IT OFF! IT'S THAT DARN DUPLICATE AND YOU KNOW IT!

MAN, HE'S GONE TOO FAR! I DON'T MIND IF HE CLEANS MY ROOM AND GETS GOOD GRADES, BUT BY GOLLY, I DRAW THE LINE AT BEING NICE TO SUSIE! CAN'T THAT DUPLICATE TELL SHE'S A *GIRL*?!

OH, I THINK HE'S FIGURED THAT OUT. I SAW HIM CUTTING HEARTS OUT OF RED CONSTRUCTION PAPER!

WAUGH!

.. AND WHO COULD MAKE MY HEART FEEL WOOZY? ONLY THOU, MY FAIR SWEET SUSIE.

DON'T TELL ME MY DUPLICATE IS WRITING SUSIE MASH NOTES!!

YOU LITTLE CHARMER, YOU!

I'M THE DICTATOR-FOR-LIFE OF THE GET RID OF SLIMY GIRLS CLUB! MY REPUTATION! MY HONOR! MY PRINCIPLES! WE'VE GOT TO STOP HIM!

OH NO! HE'S NOT IN MY ROOM! HE MUST BE ON HIS WAY TO SUSIE'S HOUSE!

YOU'RE PROBABLY GETTING SMOOCHES RIGHT NOW! BIG WET ONES, I BET!

MORE SARCASM?! YOU COME HERE AGAIN AND I'LL CLOBBER YOU, CALVIN.

Drawing the strip as if it were a soap opera strip is a fun visual surprise, and the "serious" pictures make the dialogue even more ludicrous. For the sa
satire, I wish I'd drawn this more stylishly, the way the best cartoonists of those strips did.

An animal perspective sheds some light on religious questions.

I worked on various versions of this poem, off and on, for several months. Originally I intended to illustrate the poem lavishly and use it for a book, but I never had the ti[...] I got the new Sunday format, I was eager to try things I couldn't previously do, so I drew up this version for a Sunday strip.

PAUL GAUGUIN ASKED, "WHENCE DO WE COME? WHAT ARE WE? WHERE ARE WE GOING?"

WELL, I DON'T KNOW ABOUT ANYONE ELSE, BUT *I* CAME FROM MY ROOM, I'M A KID WITH BIG PLANS, AND I'M GOING OUTSIDE! SEE YA LATER!

SAY, WHO THE HECK IS PAUL GAUGUIN ANYWAY?

I still think this strip is funny.

WHEN I GROW UP, I'M NOT GOING TO READ THE NEWSPAPER AND I'M NOT GOING TO FOLLOW COMPLEX ISSUES AND I'M NOT GOING TO VOTE.

THAT WAY I CAN COMPLAIN THAT THE GOVERNMENT DOESN'T REPRESENT ME.

THEN, WHEN EVERYTHING GOES DOWN THE TUBES, I CAN SAY THE SYSTEM DOESN'T WORK AND JUSTIFY MY FURTHER LACK OF PARTICIPATION.

AN INGENIOUSLY SELF-FULFILLING PLAN.

IT'S A LOT MORE FUN TO BLAME THINGS THAN TO FIX THEM.

A political cartoon does not have to have labels written across everything, or make its point with a sledgehammer.

The late twentieth-century drug of choice.

LOOK HOBBES, THIS WORLD IS KIND OF LIKE TV.

A CASUAL OBSERVER MIGHT EVEN CONFUSE THE TWO. BUT IF YOU NOTICE, HERE THE COLORS ARE LESS INTENSE AND THE PEOPLE ARE UGLIER.

ALSO, I SEE THAT SEVERAL MINUTES CAN GO BY WITHOUT A SINGLE CAR CHASE, EXPLOSION, MURDER OR PAT PERSONAL EXCHANGE.

WHY SETTLE FOR LESS, HMM?

SHH, THIS IS MY FAVORITE DEODORANT COMMERCIAL.

OH GREATEST OF THE MASS MEDIA, THANK YOU FOR ELEVATING EMOTION, REDUCING THOUGHT, AND STIFLING IMAGINATION.

THANK YOU FOR THE ARTIFICIALITY OF QUICK SOLUTIONS AND FOR THE INSIDIOUS MANIPULATION OF HUMAN DESIRES FOR COMMERCIAL PURPOSES.

THIS BOWL OF LUKEWARM TAPIOCA REPRESENTS MY BRAIN. I OFFER IT IN HUMBLE SACRIFICE. BESTOW THY FLICKERING LIGHT FOREVER.

LOOK AT THESE TV COMMERCIALS. EACH ONE IS A JUMBLE OF LIGHTNING QUICK, UNRELATED IMAGES AND FILM TECHNIQUES.

IT DUPLICATES THE EFFECT OF RAPIDLY FLIPPING THROUGH CHANNELS. IT'S A BARRAGE OF NON-LINEAR FREE ASSOCIATION.

I GUESS THEY'RE ADMITTING THAT A 15-SECOND COMMERCIAL EXCEEDS THE AMERICAN ATTENTION SPAN BY A GOOD 14 SECONDS.

HUH? ARE YOU STILL TALKING ABOUT THAT?

I TRY TO MAKE TELEVISION-WATCHING A COMPLETE FORFEITURE OF EXPERIENCE.

NOTICE HOW I KEEP MY JAW SLACK, SO MY MOUTH HANGS OPEN. I TRY NOT TO SWALLOW EITHER, SO I DROOL, AND I KEEP MY EYES HALF-FOCUSED, SO I DON'T USE ANY MUSCLES AT ALL.

I TAKE A PASSIVE ENTERTAINMENT AND EXTEND THE PASSIVITY TO MY ENTIRE BEING. I WALLOW IN MY LACK OF PARTICIPATION AND RESPONSE. I'M UTTERLY INERT.

I'M GOING TO LEAVE BEFORE YOU START ATTRACTING FLIES.

I CAN ALMOST FEEL MY NEURAL TRANSMITTERS SHUTTING DOWN.

For some time, I've used Calvin's snowmen as a way to make fun of the art world. I enjoy studying art, but the field certainly attracts its share of pretentious blowhards.

The initial thrill of being able to design my Sunday strip layouts was soon tempered by the difficulty of it. A confusing layout will obstruct the flow of the story, so it's impo[rtant]
the design provides a logical path for the eye. The new Sunday strips take two or three times as long to draw as the old Sunday strips.

Several months after returning from my first sabbatical, I found myself behind on deadlines and sending out material I wasn't satisfied with. This happens occasionally, and it always sends me into a tailspin, because I get discouraged and write even worse material. The strip can be a monster sometimes, and I illustrated my situation in a story where Calvin quiets his monsters by throwing them garbage.

THE ALIENS CAME
    FROM A FAR DISTANT WORLD
IN A LARGE YELLOW SHIP
    THAT BLINKED AS IT TWIRLED.
IT ROUNDED THE MOON,
    AND ENTERED OUR SKY.
WE KNEW THEY HAD COME
    BUT WE DIDN'T KNOW WHY.

BRIGHT THE NEXT MORNING,
    WITH NOISY COMMOTION,
THE SHIP SLOWLY MOVED
    OUT OVER THE OCEAN.
IT LOWERED A TUBE
    AND DRAINED THE WHOLE SEA
FOR TRANSPORT BACK HOME
    TO THEIR GALAXY.

THE TUBE THEN SUCKED UP
    THE CLOUDS AND THE AIR,
CAUSING NO SMALL AMOUNT
    OF EARTHLING DESPAIR.
WITH NOTHING TO BREATHE,
    WE STARTED TO DIE.
"HELP US! PLEASE STOP!"
    WAS THE PUBLIC OUTCRY.

A HATCH OPENED UP
    AND THE ALIENS SAID,
"WE'RE SORRY TO LEARN
    THAT YOU SOON WILL BE DEAD,
BUT THOUGH YOU MAY FIND
    THIS SLIGHTLY MACABRE,
WE PREFER YOUR EXTINCTION
    TO THE LOSS OF OUR JOB."

THAT'S MY SCIENCE F
STORY. THINK IT'S
FAR-FETCHED?

NOT
REA

In recent years, the strip has had more overt commentary to it. I didn't set out with that as a goal, but I guess that's where my mind is. I always try to keep the strip funny
to the characters, because preachy cartoons get tiresome quickly.

WHITHER GOEST THOU, YOUNG ROGUE? CAN THERE YET REMAIN SOME VILLANY THOU HAST NOT COMMITTED?

THOU DOST WRONG ME! FAITH, I KNOW NOT WHERE I WANDER. METHINKS THE MOST CAPRICIOUS ZEPHYR HATH MORE DESIGN THAN I. BUT LO: DO NOT DETAIN ME, FOR I AM RESOLV'D TO QUIT THIS PLACE FORTHWITH.

AY, BUT HEAR YOU THIS, I'LL SOON KNOW THY BUSINESS. GET THEE GONE, WASTREL!

BY MY TROTH, I AM OFF.

HOLY SCHLA*MOLY*, ISN'T THERE A COP SHOW ON WHERE THEY TALK LIKE REAL PEOPLE?

SHHH.

I watched a Shakespeare play on TV without understanding a word of it. It gave me an idea for a strip, though.

MOM DOESN'T UNDERSTAND COMIC BOOKS.

SHE DOESN'T REALIZE THAT COMIC BOOKS DEAL WITH SERIOUS ISSUES OF THE DAY. TODAY'S SUPERHEROES FACE TOUGH MORAL DILEMMAS.

COMIC BOOKS AREN'T JUST ESCAPIST FANTASY. THEY'RE SOPHISTICATED SOCIAL CRITIQUES.

IS AMAZON GIRL'S SUPER POWER THE ABILITY TO SQUEEZE THAT FIGURE INTO THAT SUIT?

NAH, THEY ALL CAN DO THAT.

You can make your superhero a psychopath, you can draw gut-splattering violence, and you can call it a "graphic novel," but comic books are still incredibly stupid.

It's sometimes sort of frightening where my mind will go if I let it. Who *was* that guy?!

People will pay for what they want, but not for what they need.

...cling, so I occasionally do some bike strips. Other cyclists seem to enjoy them, so it's tempting to do more of them, but bike strips risk being self-indulgent. A lot of ...do golf strips, and I find those insufferable. When I do a bike strip, I always try to focus on Calvin's dad's personality, so it's not just a joke for particular hobbyists.

Panel 1: HERE'S AN INTERESTING ARTICLE. THE TOP FIVE GUM BRANDS ARE COMPARED IN TERMS OF FLAVOR RETENTION, ELASTICITY, BUBBLE CAPACITY AND CHEWING REBOUND.

Panel 2: THE COMPUTER GRAPH SHOWS THE RESULTS, COMPENSATING FOR VARIOUS SALIVA ACIDITIES. IF YOU KNOW YOUR pH, THIS REALLY HELPS YOU CHOOSE THE PROPER GUM FOR YOUR CHEWING STYLE.

Panel 3: WHAT KIND OF NUT WOULD CARE ABOUT ALL THIS?! — EVERYONE! THIS IS HARD DATA! IT LETS YOU QUANTIFY YOUR ENJOYMENT!

Panel 4: I THOUGHT FUN WAS SUPPOSED TO BE FUN. — WELL I PREFER TO TRUST THE EXPERTS.

There are magazines now for every hobby and obsession, and they're all the same. Calvin's *Chewing* magazine is based on the cycling magazines I read. The silly articles I make up are so close to the real thing, it's hardly satire.

Panel 1: LOOK, HOBBES. THERE'S A QUIZ IN MY NEW ISSUE OF *CHEWING* MAGAZINE. "DOES YOUR GUM DELIVER? 10 QUESTIONS SHOW WHAT YOU COULD BE MISSING!"

Panel 2: LET'S SEE HOW MY GUM DOES. "1. HOW HARD IS YOUR GUM AT THE BEGINNING? A) ROCK-LIKE OR BRITTLE B) PLEASANTLY FIRM C) SQUISHY OR BENDY"

Panel 3: HMM... MY GUM IS PRETTY HARD AT FIRST. I'LL MARK "A".

Panel 4: GOSH, I'VE GOT NEGATIVE FIVE POINTS ALREADY! I'M NOT GETTING ALL THE PERFORMANCE I'M ENTITLED TO! — I WONDER WHAT PEOPLE KNEW BEFORE THERE WERE MAGAZINE QUIZZES.

AT 35,000 FEET, THE ENGINES OF FLIGHT 430 EXPLODE FOR NO REASON!

WITH PLUMES OF DENSE SMOKE TRAILING FROM THE WINGS, THE GIANT AIRCRAFT PLUMMETS OUT OF CONTROL!

MEANWHILE, A 50-CAR FREIGHT TRAIN HITS A PENNY ON THE RAIL AT 80 MILES AN HOUR AND JUMPS THE TRACKS, DRAGGING HALF A MILLION TONS OF METAL INTO THE AIR BEHIND IT!

caLViN aNd HObbEs by WATTERSON

...EAK COINCIDENCE, BOTH ...AND THE TRAIN ARE ...ING ON *ONE SPOT*,...WHERE ...C PLATES IN THE EARTH'S ...HAVE JUST BEGUN ...O SHIFT!

THAT SPOT IS THE HOUSE OF FARMER BROWN, WHO, AT THIS MOMENT, IS UNAWARE OF A GAS LEAK AS HE ATTEMPTS TO LIGHT HIS STOVE!

AS HE STRIKES THE MATCH, HE CASUALLY GLANCES OUT THE KITCHEN WINDOW.

HIS EYE TWITCHES INVOLUNTARILY.

CAN'T WE PLAY SOMETHING ELSE?

...lvin's better build-ups.

I entered a school safety poster contest when I was a kid. I labored over a careful drawing of Snoopy, which got me disqualified. I was crushed, but it was a pretty good lesson about the value of originality. Calvin, of course, has the opposite problem.

WANT TO HELP ME MAKE A POSTER?

SURE. WHAT'S IT FOR?

IT'S A SCHOOL CONTEST. WE'RE SUPPOSED TO DO TRAFFIC SAFETY POSTERS. THE WINNER GETS FIVE BUCKS!

WOW!

THINK OF IT! WE'LL BE RICH! AND THEN THERE'S THE FAME AND GLORY! I TELL YOU, THIS COULD BE OUR TICKET OUT OF THIS TWO-BIT DUMP!

SOUNDS GOOD. WHAT'S OUR WINNING POSTER GOING TO SAY?

THAT'S WHERE **YOU** COME IN.

OUR TRAFFIC SAFETY POSTER NEEDS A CATCHY SLOGAN THAT PROMOTES AWARENESS AND CAUTION. ANY IDEAS?

HOW ABOUT, "DON'T LOOK INTO CAR HEADLIGHTS AND FREEZE, BECAUSE YOU'LL EITHER GET RUN OVER OR SHOT!"

I'LL CHECK THE STATISTICS, BUT I DON'T THINK THAT HAPPENS TO MANY PEOPLE.

THERE'S MORE TO THIS WORLD THAN JUST PEOPLE, YOU KNOW.

HEY DAD, I'M DOING A TRAFFIC SAFETY POSTER. DO YOU HAVE ANY IDEAS FOR A SLOGAN?

SURE! "CYCLISTS HAVE A RIGHT TO THE ROAD TOO, YOU NOISY, POLLUTING, INCONSIDERATE MANIACS! I HOPE GAS GOES UP TO EIGHT BUCKS A GALLON!"

THANKS, DAD. I'LL GO ASK MOM.

WHY? THAT'S A GREAT SLOGAN!

MOM SUGGESTED THE SLOGAN, "BEFORE YOU CROSS, LOOK EACH WAY... AND YOU'LL GET HOME SAFE EACH DAY."

THAT'S KIND OF CATCHY.

YEAH, BUT I LIKE MY IDEA BETTER.

"BE CAREFUL, OR BE ROADKILL!"

I SUPPOSE THAT LENDS ITSELF MORE TO YOUR PARTICULAR BRAND OF ILLUSTRATION.

I HOPE I HAVE ENOUGH CADMIUM RED.

OUR POSTER DIDN'T WIN?

I STILL CAN'T BELIEVE IT.

WHAT A MISCARRIAGE OF JUSTICE! THIS CONTEST WAS A JOKE! OBVIOUSLY THE JUDGES WERE BIASED AGAINST US FROM THE START!

WELL, THE IMPORTANT THING IS THAT WE TRIED OUR BEST.

THE *IMPORTANT* THING IS THAT WE *LOST*!

OOPS, I ALWAYS FORGET THE PURPOSE OF COMPETITION IS TO DIVIDE PEOPLE INTO WINNERS AND LOSERS.

WHAT'S THE POINT OF TRYING IF YOU CAN'T BE A WINNER?

DAD, MY POSTER DIDN'T WIN THE CONTEST! I THINK THE JUDGES WERE ON THE TAKE AND THE WHOLE THING WAS RIGGED!

I WANT YOU TO CALL THE SCHOOL BOARD, HAVE THEM DECLARE FRAUD, AND MAKE THEM TAKE THE PRIZE AWAY FROM SUSIE AND GIVE IT TO *ME*!

CALVIN, LOSING IS A PART OF LIFE. YOU SHOULD LEARN TO BE A GOOD SPORT ABOUT IT AND KEEP THINGS IN PERSPECTIVE. AFTER ALL, WINNING ISN'T EVERYTHING.

IS THAT REALLY WHAT THEY BELIEVE ON THE PLANET YOU'RE FROM?

YOU'VE BEEN WATCHING ATHLETIC SHOE ADS AGAIN, HAVEN'T YOU?

I'd like a suit like Calvin's dad wears.

Most ignorance is willful.

My wife is very funny, although sometimes unintentionally. I exaggerated one of her abrupt subject shifts for this strip.

I read a book of art criticism that was an avalanche of politically correct, New Age, academic jargon and art-speak. The writing so annoyed me that I started underlining the worst passages of gibberish for future reference, and I've adapted it for several strips. Calvin, of course, quickly grasps the purpose of such writing.

I also hate pop psychobabble.

As somebody said, we all want to go to heaven, but nobody wants to do what it takes to get there.

I did pretty well at school, but I don't remember it with much fondness.

If Calvin thinks school is like this, wait until he gets his first job.

Stupendous Man hasn't given me as many ideas as I hoped, but I like this story because of the various viewpoints it juggles.

189

WHERE'S CALVIN? DIDN'T HE COME BACK FROM THE DRINKING FOUNTAIN?

I'LL BET HE'S AT HIS LOCKER, MISS WORMWOOD. HE BROUGHT SOMETHING SECRET IN A PAPER BAG TODAY THAT HE SAID WOULD HELP HIM ON THE TEST.

FIVE YEARS UNTIL RETIREMENT FIVE YEARS UNTIL RETIREMENT

STUPENDOUS MAN'S STUPENDOUS POWERS ARE OF NO AVAIL IN THIS CUNNING TRAP! ZOUNDS! IT'S STUPENDOUS MAN'S FIENDISH NEMESIS, THE CRAB TEACHER, COMING TO FINISH HIM OFF!

CALVIN?

LET'S SEE IF CALVIN GOT WHATEVER WAS IN HIS LOCKER.

KA-CHUNK

WITH STUPENDOUS MUSCLES OF MAGNITUDE, STUPENDOUS MAN BREAKS FREE!!

WHAT ON EARTH?!

S ...FOR STUPENDOUS!
T ...FOR TIGER, FEROCITY OF!
U ...FOR UNDERWEAR, RED!
P ...FOR POWER, INCREDIBLE!
E ...FOR EXCELLENT PHYSIQUE!
N ...FOR ...UM... SOMETHING...HM, WELL, I'LL COME BACK TO THAT...
D ...FOR DETERMINATION!
U ...FOR... WAIT, HOW DO YOU SPELL THIS? IS IT "I"??

IT'S NOT ENOUGH THAT WE HAVE TO BE DISCIPLINARIANS. NOW WE NEED TO BE PSYCHOLOGISTS.

YOUR NEFARIOUS SCHEME WILL NEVER SUCCEED!

STUPENDOUS MAN ESCAPES! A CRIMSON BOLT BURSTS THROUGH THE AIR!

CALVIN, COME BACK HERE!

NOW IT'S OFF TO APPLY MY STUPENDOUS POWERS OF CONCENTRATION TO THE HISTORY TEST OF MY ALTER EGO, MILD-MANNERED CALVIN!

TA-DAAA! HAVE NO FEAR, BOYS AND GIRLS! I'M STUPENDOUS MAN, CHAMPION OF LIBERTY AND JUSTICE!

TRY TO RESTRAIN YOURSELVES, GIRLS! I'M JUST HERE TO DO CALVIN'S TEST.

HE LIVES ON YOUR STREET, DOESN'T HE?

I HARDLY EVEN KNOW HIM, CANDACE!

STUPENDOUS MAN'S STUPENDOUS KNOWLEDGE LETS HIM COMPLETE THE TEST WITH STUPENDOUS SPEED! 1492! THE BATTLE OF LEXINGTON! TROTSKY! THE COTTON GIN!

ANOTHER TRIUMPH FOR VIRTUE AND RIGHT! AND NOW, WITH A WHOOSH, STUPENDOUS MAN IS OFF INTO THE SKY! SO LONG, KIDS! ALWAYS BRUSH YOUR TEETH! KAPWINGGG!

CLASS, DID CALVIN COME IN HERE?! HAS ANYONE SEEN HIM?

HERE I AM, MISS WORMWOOD! BOY, WAS I THIRSTY!

...! A SCHOOL DAY BREAK ...AY AND EXERCISE. ...DOES SUSIE REALIZE ...UCH EXERCISE SHE ...ABOUT TO GET!

SHE TURNS AT THE SOUND OF RUNNING FEET BEHIND HER. HAVE HER FRIENDS COME TO JOIN HER?

... GRIM EFFICIENCY ... DOGS, THE ...RS HAVE A ...AL!

NO! IT'S A PACK OF FEROCIOUS DEINONYCHUS DINOSAURS!!

SCREAMING, SUSIE HURLS HERSELF TOWARD THE SCHOOL DOORS, BUT THE PACK IS CLOSING IN!

ACROSS THE PLAYGROUND, STUDENTS HUDDLE IN STUPEFIED HORROR! WHICH ONE OF THEM WILL BE NEXT?

THUS THE WEAK AND STUPID ARE WEEDED OUT IN A HEARTLESS, BUT ESSENTIAL, NATURAL SELECTION, KEEPING THE HUMAN POPULATION IN CHECK.

...AT LEAST, THAT'S HOW IT OUGHT TO BE.

THANK YOU FOR THAT TASTELESS AND ENTIRELY UNINFORMATIVE REPORT ON OVERPOPULATION. SEE ME AFTER CLASS.

YA LIKE THAT, SUSIE??

was drawn before the movie *Jurassic Park* came out, and the deinonychus here is a smaller relative of the velociraptors in the film. I stopped doing strips for about six months when the movie was released. A few little drawings can't create the visceral response of large-screen computer special effects, n't want Calvin's imagination to look less vivid for the comparison.

This is my dad. No exaggeration.

I'm sure they're working on this.

tion is not always appreciated. In the last panel here, I faded a narrow range of colors to create an atmospheric effect, and I think this is one of my more
e landscapes.

Right lesson, wrong time.

Calvin's vocabulary puzzles some readers, but Calvin has never been a literal six-year-old. Cumbersome words are funny to me, and I like Calvin's ability to precisely articulate stupid ideas.

…e larger Sunday strip, I find I can often tell a story with greater nuance by eliminating the dialogue altogether.

THROWING THESE SNOWBALLS WOULD GIVE ME IMMEDIATE AND CERTAIN PLEASURE.

REFRAINING FROM THROWING THESE SNOWBALLS IN THE HOPE OF BEING REWARDED AT CHRISTMAS IS DELAYED AND **UN**CERTAIN PLEASURE.

AS USUAL, GOODNESS HARDLY PUTS UP A FIGHT.

I often use the Christmas season for Calvin to wrestle with good and evil. He wants to be good, but for the wrong reasons.

GRAPHIC VIOLENCE IN THE MEDIA.

DOES IT GLAMORIZE VIOLENCE? SURE. DOES IT DESENSITIZE US TO VIOLENCE? OF COURSE. DOES IT HELP US TOLERATE VIOLENCE? YOU BET. DOES IT STUNT OUR EMPATHY FOR OUR FELLOW BEINGS? HECK YES.

DOES IT **CAUSE** VIOLENCE? ...WELL, THAT'S HARD TO PROVE.

THE TRICK IS TO ASK THE RIGHT QUESTION.

What's to debate?

LOOK, A DEAD BIRD!

IT MUST'VE HIT THE WINDOW.

ISN'T IT BEAUTIFUL? IT'S SO DELICATE.

SIGHHH... ONCE IT'S TOO LATE, YOU APPRECIATE WHAT A MIRACLE LIFE IS.

YOU REALIZE THAT NATURE IS RUTHLESS AND OUR EXISTENCE IS VERY FRAGILE, TEMPORARY, AND PRECIOUS.

Calvin and Hobbes by WATTERSON

BUT TO GO ON WITH YOUR DAILY AFFAIRS, YOU CAN'T REALLY THINK ABOUT THAT.

...WHICH IS PROBABLY WHY EVERYONE TAKES THE WORLD FOR GRANTED AND WHY WE ACT SO THOUGHTLESSLY.

IT'S VERY CONFUSING.

I SUPPOSE IT WILL ALL MAKE SENSE WHEN WE GROW UP.

NO DOUBT.

...ng is a way for me to muse about the nature of things, and I sketched a dead bird I found with reflections similar to Calvin's. Not many Sunday strips begin ...first panel like this, and I wondered if readers would find it offensive. In fact, I received several moving letters from people who had suffered losses and ...the strip meaningful. Sharing with people, I'm always impressed by how they share back.

Hamster Huey and the Gooey Kablooie (like "the Noodle Incident" I've referred to in several strips) is left to the reader's imagination, where it's sure to be more outrageous.

I don't pray for this, but it's the case anyway.

f my strips end up being little sermons, and this can be annoying and sappy if it's not handled lightly. One of the ongoing jokes in the strip is that Calvin usually ne wrong lesson from his experiences, if he learns anything at all. Calvin's expression in the last panel suggests that he is resisting the moral here too.

I would suggest that it's not the medium, but the quality of perception and expression, that determines the significance of art. But what would a cartoonist know?

I don't know how much Hobbes helps Calvin gain perspective, but Hobbes certainly helps me.

ow why we're wired this way, but we are.

I LIKE FOLLOWING THE NEWS! NEWS ORGANIZATIONS KNOW I WON'T SIT STILL FOR ANY SERIOUS DISCUSSION OF COMPLEX AND BORING ISSUES.

THEY GIVE ME WHAT I WANT: ANTICS, EMOTIONAL CONFRONTATION, SOUND BITES, SCANDAL, SOB STORIES AND POPULARITY POLLS ALL PACKAGED AS A SOAP OPERA AND HORSE RACE! IT'S VERY ENTERTAINING.

THEN COMMENTATORS WONDER WHY THE PUBLIC IS CYNICAL ABOUT POLITICS.

YOU CAN TELL THIS IS AN IN-DEPTH STORY, BECAUSE IT'S GOT AN ARTICLE NEXT TO THE CHART.

Newspaper editors sometimes seem to resent that they have to run comics. Well, sometimes I resent being in their newspapers.

LOOK AT HOW PEOPLE ARE PORTRAYED IN COMIC STRIPS. THE WOMEN ARE INDECISIVE WHINERS, NAGGING SHREWS, AND BIMBOS!

AND THE MEN ARE NO BETTER. THEY'RE BEFUDDLED MORONS, HEAVY DRINKERS, GLUTTONS, AND LAZY GOOF-OFFS! EVERYONE IS INCOMPETENT, UNAPPRECIATED, AND UNSUCCESSFUL!

WHAT KIND OF INSIDIOUS SOCIAL PROGRAMMING IS THIS?! NO WONDER THE WORLD'S SUCH A MESS! I DEMAND POLITICALLY CORRECT, MORALLY UPLIFTING ROLE MODELS IN THE FUNNIES!

YES, WE ALL KNOW HOW FUNNY GOOD ROLE MODELS ARE.

AND LOOK, ALL THE KIDS ARE OBNOXIOUS BRATS!

Comic strips have historically been full of ugly stereotypes, the hallmark of writers too lazy to honestly observe the world. Offended parties often suggest the further sanitization of the comics, but one of the great strengths of cartooning is its ability to criticize through distortion. The trick is to remember that the way we describe things reveals the way we think. The cartoonist who resorts to stereotypes reveals his own bigotry.

part of being a cartoonist is the ever-present opportunity to be silly. This is a dumb strip, but I sure had fun with it.

This is how I remember summer. When the strip captures real moments—without making them saccharine and tidy—my work is very gratifying.

CARTOONING AND *CALVIN AND HOBBES*

I don't think of comics as just entertainment. It's a rare privilege to be able to talk to millions of people on a given day, so I'm eager to say something meaningful when I can. There is always pressure to write some snappy one-liner that will buy me another twenty-four hours of lead time on deadlines, but nothing depresses me like thinking I've become a joke factory to fill newspaper space. Whenever possible, I use the strip to talk about the things that are important to me.

I think the best comics (like the best novels, paintings, etc.) are personal, idiosyncratic works that reflect a unique and honest sensibility. To attract and keep an audience, art must entertain, but the significance of any art lies in its ability to express truths—to reveal and help us understand our world. Comic strips, in their own humble way, are capable of doing this.

The best comics expose human nature and help us laugh at our own stupidity and hypocrisy. They indulge in exaggeration and absurdity, helping us to see the world with fresh eyes and reminding us how important it is to play and be silly. Comics depict the ordinary, mundane events of our lives and help us remember the importance of tiny moments. They cleverly sum up our unexpressed thoughts and emotions. Sometimes they show the world from the perspective of children and animals, encouraging us to be innocent for a moment. The best comics, that is to say, are fun house mirrors that distort appearances only to help us recognize, and laugh at, our essential characteristics.

Surprise is the essence of humor, and nothing is more surprising than truth. When cartoons dig beyond glib punch lines, cheap sentimentality, and tidy stories to deeper, truthful experiences, they can really touch people and connect us all. As frustrated as I am by the way this business works, I continue to believe that comics are an art form capable of any level of beauty, intelligence, and sophistication.

I've written and drawn over three thousand *Calvin and Hobbes* strips now, and to the extent that the strip reflects my interests, values, and thoughts, my cartoons are a sort of self-portrait. The longer I've worked, the more I've used the strip to explore personal issues. When I come up with an idea that surprises me, I'm happy to offer it to anyone who shares my interests. I'm flattered when people respond to my work, but I don't feel accountable to public demand. Trying to please people encourages calculation, and the strip is valuable to me only insofar as it's honest and sincere.

It's not hard to write jokes—good characters will always have something amusing to say about their situation—but it's very difficult to keep the strip's world energized and expansive year after year. At the beginning of a strip, virtually every installment explores new territory, but it's frightening how fast stories and situations become predictable. Today's funny innovation is tomorrow's stale formula.

My early strips look crude and forced to me now, but the characters were still introducing themselves to me. The first couple of years were exploratory efforts to create an engaging world and rounded characters. I began writing longer stories when I saw how they added dimension to the characters' personalities and relationships. Lately, I've had trouble writing extended narratives that satisfy me, and I've been doing fewer of them. Instead, my enthusiasm has drifted to the visual possibilities of the larger Sunday strip. Over the years, *Calvin and Hobbes* has changed directions, but I don't control where it goes. When everything is working, I'm more surprised by the strip's destination than anybody.

The trick to writing a comic strip is to cultivate a mental playfulness—a natural curiosity and eagerness to learn. If I keep my eyes open and follow my interests, sooner or later the effort yields questions, thoughts, and ideas—unexpected paths into new territory. Like Calvin, I just head out into the yard in search of weirdness, and with the right attitude, I make discoveries.

Putting myself in the head of a fictitious six-year-old and a tiger encourages me to be more alert and inquisitive than I would otherwise be. Sometimes I resent the pressure to exploit every waking moment for strip ideas, but at its best, the strip makes me examine events and live more thoughtfully. I love the solitude of this work and the opportunity to work with ideas that interest me. This is the greatest reward of cartooning for me.

I've always loved cartoons. With *Calvin and Hobbes*, I've tried to return some of the fun, magic, and beauty I've enjoyed in other comics. It's been immensely satisfying to draw *Calvin and Hobbes*, and I will always be grateful to have had the opportunity to work in this wonderful art form.